John Flamsteed

The
First Astronomer Royal
at Greenwich

JOHN FLAMSTEED
THE
FIRST ASTRONOMER ROYAL
at GREENWICH

John L. Birks Ph.D.

AVON BOOKS
1 Dovedale Studios
465 Battersea Park Road
London SW11 4LR

Printed and bound in the U.K.

Avon Books

London
First Published 1999
© John L. Birks Ph.D., 1999
ISBN 1 86033 568 3

ACKNOWLEDGEMENTS

I would like to acknowledge the encouragement I have received from friends and colleagues in the Swansea Astronomical Society while writing this book, who made me persevere at times when I might otherwise have given up the project.

My grateful thanks are due in particular to Dr. Frances Willmoth of Cambridge University who is now completing the editing of the final volume of John Flamsteed's *Correspondence* and who took time to correct several mistakes in my preliminary script. Her incomparable knowledge of Flamsteed and the science of the time in which he lived are only equalled by her willingness to share that knowledge with others. Any errors which still exist are, of course, my own responsibility.

I would also like to thank the staffs of the National Maritime Museum at Greenwich, the National Portrait Gallery, the Royal Society and the Derby Museum and Art Gallery for their assistance in obtaining copies of the material in their collections for use as illustrations in this book.

In addition, thanks are due to the National Maritime Museum for kindly granting me permission to use excerpts from their Monograph No. 52, 1982, entitled "The Preface to John Flamsteed's *Historia Coelestis Britannica*", which are Crown copyright.

John Flamsteed would no doubt have been pleased to know that amateur astronomy is still practised in Denby Village near to where he was born. I would like to express my thanks to Peter and Adrian Bestwick of Denby Village for showing me various celestial objects through their 6 inch refractor telescope over a period of many years.

Caswell, Swansea.   J. L. Birks
1998

DEDICATION

Dedicated to Matthew Taunton,
who, when only eight years old,
knew something about "the obliquity of the ecliptic".

List Of Illustrations

TABLE OF CONTENTS

JOHN FLAMSTEED: ASTRONOMER ROYAL AND FELLOW
OF THE ROYAL SOCIETY.

This portrait, now in the possession of the Royal Society, shows Flamsteed at
around 34 years of age. It has been identified by Dr. Frances Willmoth as being
by the artist Thomas Murray and is mentioned in Margaret Flamsteed's will

Reproduced by kind permission of the President and Council of the Royal Society.

CHAPTER I
The Early Years

T he sprawling parish of Denby lies about eight miles north of the city of Derby and still consists largely of agricultural fields, hills and small woodlands. The wave of industrialisation has washed over this rural area and now that coal-mining and the more recent open-cast mining have ceased, the countryside is reverting to something more resembling what it might have been like in the 17th Century.

It was here in Denby Village, on August 19th, 1646, at 7.15 in the evening, that a child was born who was later to become one of the most notable men of science in England: a Master of Arts of the University of Cambridge, an elected Fellow of the Royal Society and appointed by King Charles the Second as the first "Astronomer Royal". No one could have foreseen the future which lay in store for John Flamsteed, when he was born in that quiet and unpretentious Derbyshire village but sufficient interest in astrology existed in those days that his father carefully noted the exact minute of his birth. And in a similar fashion, some twenty nine years later, John Flamsteed recorded the laying of the foundation stone of the Royal Observatory at Greenwich, on the 10th of August, 1675, at 3 hours and 14 minutes *"post meridiem"* and he drew a horoscope chart for its future. Not that the young John Flamsteed believed that the future was ordained by the stars and planets, for he wrote on the Greenwich Observatory chart in Latin *"Risum teneatis amici"* - "May this keep you laughing, my friends." Astrology and the casting of horoscopes remained a popular curiosity in the minds of many people in those days, even amongst the scientifically educated such as Johannes Kepler (1571 - 1630) and these superstitions had some influence in John Flamsteed's early years. "I found astrology to give generally strong conjectural hints, not perfect declarations," he wrote. Nevertheless, he took care not to be seen studying the works of the popular astronomer and astrologer John Gadbury too closely, "lest I should be suspected astrological."

The Flamsteed family background was essentially middle-class. John Flamsteed's father was Stephen, the third son of Mr. William Flamsteed of Little Hallam, near Ilkeston in Derbyshire, whose ancestors had come from the north of England and had lived at Hallam Mere since about the year 1500. Stephen Flamsteed had a business as a maltster in Derby and also owned lead-mines in the Peak District as well as his smallholding in Denby Village. John Flamsteed's mother, Mary, was the daughter of Mr. John Spateman, a Derby ironmonger and it might have been supposed that this young boy was fortunate to be born into such a family. However, hardship entered early into his life when Mary died on the 7th of September, 1649, less than one month after giving birth to his sister Elizabeth, leaving John only three years and two weeks old.

Some three years later, Stephen Flamsteed took a second wife, Elizabeth Bates. But again tragedy struck their home when John Flamsteed's stepmother died on November 1st, 1654, some two months after giving birth to his half-sister Katherine. The family was thus left with the father, Stephen, a widower twice over, with his son John now aged eight years and two months and two daughters, Elizabeth aged five and Katherine a baby who was only two months old. The deaths of these two mothers so soon after the birth of their daughters reminds us of the sad toll of maternal mortality in those days.

The isolated dwelling occupied by the Flamsteed family on Flamstead Lane in Denby Village, in an elevated position overlooking the Church of St. Mary the Virgin, has now been demolished. In its place is a large modern house with a yard and stables, called "Crowtrees", which bears a small plaque recording that "On this site stood the house where John Flamsteed the first Astronomer Royal was born on 19th August 1646." The house looks out over wide horizons (see figure 2) and it is not surprising that an intelligent and inquisitive child, as John Flamsteed undoubtedly was, should begin to take an interest in the sky and the weather in such a place as this. The situation of the house is such that it would give ample opportunity for observing the heavens on any clear night, being free from surrounding buildings and even today it remains well away from the lights of modern developments, which make the practice of astronomy so difficult in many places.

It seems quite possible that the family name could have been pronounced and spelt "Flamstead" originally, as that spelling is still used in Denby Village; for instance in the name of the lane which leads up to the site of the family house. Also the names of the three "houses" in the local former grammar school at Heanor were "Ray", "Howitt", and "Flamstead" - all these being the names of local gentlemen of distinction. That of Flamstead seems to relate to the first Astronomer Royal. However, the name Flamsteed was certainly used later when John contacted the Royal Society in London (the full title of which was "The Royal Society of London for the Improvement of Natural Knowledge") and this spelling was always used by him in his academic life. A similar ambiguity exists regarding the pronunciation and spelling of the name of Edmond Halley (the astronomer famous for his prediction of the 75/76 year elliptical cycle of the comet named after him), which apparently could have been Hailey, Hally, Haly, or even Hawley. In those days spelling had not become so rigid or important as it is today and there was a useful degree of flexibility! Even John Flamsteed himself, the most careful of astronomers who placed great importance on accuracy, sometimes wrote the surname of his assistant James Hodgson, who married his niece, as Hudson.

John Flamsteed was educated at the Free School, situated in St. Peter's Churchyard in Derby, near where his father carried on his malting business. This was a grammar school which gave free tuition to its pupils. Parents, however, were expected to provide the necessary books and quill-pens and also wax candles to use when the light grew dim. Most of the masters were Puritans who believed in discipline and hard work and they generally pursued practical methods of teaching with an emphasis on understanding and questioning the subject rather than learning by rote. John Flamsteed did well under their tuition. He developed a love of reading and the study of history, as well as a good knowledge of Latin - which later gave him an invaluable access to the international scientific literature of his time, which was almost entirely written in Latin.

During the summer of 1660, however, when aged 14, John Flamsteed contracted an illness whilst bathing with other boys in the swimming pool which Lord Aston had built in Derby alongside the River Derwent. Although he felt no immediate ill effect, the next morning he was overcome with general weakness and his body, thighs and legs were so swollen that he was unable to dress in his usual clothes. The treatment he was given was to rub a mixture of clay and vinegar over the affected parts of his body, which succeeded in reducing the swelling except in his joints. For the rest of his life, Flamsteed suffered with a chronic arthritis of his knees and ankles, as well as weakness in his legs and frequent headaches. This illness also cut short his education and despite his showing himself a very promising scholar, he was unable to go up to Cambridge University at that time due to his poor health. Instead he left school in May 1662, whilst still only 15 years old and afterwards continued his studies at home.

John Flamsteed would dearly have wished to go on to university as the school-master had suggested to his father but Stephen Flamsteed thought that study seemed to aggravate his illness. John, however, thought that at the university he might have made contact with clever physicians who could perhaps have provided a cure. He recognised that his poor health might become a long-standing problem, writing that "My bodily weakness will not permit me action. My mind is fitted for the contemplation of God and his works." He therefore "desired learning and divinity" even from his youth. He was grateful for his father's attention to his illness and the efforts he made to find a cure and wrote that he thanked God that his father was reasonably well-off so that he could pay for such treatment as might restore his health.

Figure 1.
Plaque on the site of Flamsteed's birthplace, Denby Village.

Figure 2.
View over Denby Village, Derbyshire.

A curious story, concerning John Flamsteed's school-days appeared in William Hutton's *History of Derby* which was published in 1791. The author recounts a tale which he had heard from an old man, Mr. John Webb, about 50 years earlier. Webb alleged that the young John Flamsteed, together with other youths, had committed a highway robbery for which they had been tried in court and condemned. It was said that only by the intercession of influential friends was Flamsteed granted a free pardon from King Charles the Second and this official document was supposed to have been found amongst his papers after his death in 1719. It is of course notoriously difficult to prove conclusively that an alleged incident never, in fact, occurred but from all the circumstances of Flamsteed's life at this time it would seem that any suggestion of his having taken part in a violent robbery would be completely out of character with what is known for certain about him. John Flamsteed was inclined to be a studious, thoughtful person and was tolerably well-off, with neither the necessity nor the disposition to become a forceful criminal. Also, in the very same year that King Charles came to the throne (1660), Flamsteed suffered the illness which dogged him for the rest of his life, making him unable to take part in any vigorous physical attack. It is therefore very unlikely that at any time after the accession of King Charles to the throne, Flamsteed could have participated in a violent offence such as was alleged. Also, it is inconceivable that the king would have appointed as his "Astronomer Royal" a person to whom he had granted pardon for a capital crime only a few years earlier. Finally, it seems improbable that a written document, such as the royal pardon, would not have been destroyed, either by Flamsteed himself during the further 60 years of his life or by his executrixes (his wife and his niece) if they found such a paper amongst his belongings after his death. In his *Account of the Revd. John Flamsteed*, published in 1835, Francis Baily refuted these allegations of Flamsteed's detractors and removed this stain on his character beyond reasonable doubt. Flamsteed showed himself quite capable of defending his interests by legal means in later life, but to take on the mantle of a highway robber whilst barely into his teens would have been quite beyond his physical capabilities or his mental characteristics!

By the time he left school, John Flamsteed was known as a sensible and intelligent youth who came from a good family background and appeared to have scholarly potential. But he was already troubled by the chronic ill-health that was to affect him from time to time throughout the rest of his life.

CHAPTER II

First Steps in Astronomy

After leaving the Free Grammar School in Derby in May 1662, John Flamsteed continued to study by himself at home. His father also gave him some tuition in elementary arithmetic and the use of fractions when business affairs allowed this. Also, being the only son, he was expected to help Stephen Flamsteed in the family business and in dealing with the various servants they employed. John had a younger sister and a half-sister at home but they had no mother to run the household.

Very soon afterwards, in July 1662, Flamsteed turned his main interest to the study of mathematics and astronomy when he was lent a book entitled *De Sphaera Mundi* by Johannes Sacrobosco - a 13th Century English astronomer who had studied Ptolemy's *Almagest* and the works of the early Arab astronomers. This book was in Latin but Flamsteed's schooling made him sufficiently competent in that language that he was able to read it. Sacrobosco's book fascinated the young Flamsteed and, living as he was in a secluded part of the countryside, he was able to back up his reading with his own astronomical observations - with no difficulty except that his equipment was of an elementary kind and home-made.

John Flamsteed was a practical person as well as a capable scholar and he ground and polished his own lenses in order to make himself an astronomical telescope. Also, because he was not content just to observe the heavenly bodies but also wanted to be able to measure their positions in the night sky, he made himself a rough wooden quadrant (See Appendix 1, A) so that he could determine the angle of any object above the horizon. With his simple equipment, Flamsteed carried out observations which enabled him to construct a table showing the variations in the Sun's altitude on a daily basis. Also, he became interested in the partial solar eclipses which occurred when the Moon passed between the Earth and the Sun in the daytime. The first such eclipse he observed, which, according to Francis Baily, took place on the 12th of September, 1662 (when he was only just 16 years old), marked the commencement of John Flamsteed's astronomical career. He was already, at this tender age, a keen observer of the sky with exceptional practical skills, though largely self-taught.

In the New Year of 1663, Stephen Flamsteed sent John to Uttoxeter in Staffordshire to try to improve his health and whilst resting there he read a book by the astronomer Thomas Fale entitled *The Art of Dialling*, which was concerned with the design and construction of sundials. This book also fired his enthusiasm and he proceeded to calculate a table of the Sun's altitude at different times of the year as seen from the equator, from the tropics, and from latitude 53 degrees north (Derby is at latitude 52 degrees 55 minutes north). In this exercise, he was assisted by the *Table of Sines* given in Fale's book and no doubt Flamsteed's expertise in trigonometry increased enormously at this time.

Flamsteed's interest in mathematics and astronomy was insatiable and he avidly devoured all the books on these subjects that he could lay his hands on. When he had leisure time during the summer of 1663, he read Wingate's *Canon* and Stirrup's *Art of Dialling* and Oughtred's *Canon*. All these books were on aspects of mathematics or on astronomical surveying and measuring and contained useful mathematical tables, the word "canon" coming from the Greek and signifying a straight staff used as a measuring rod. The word was later applied in various arts and sciences during the 17th Century to indicate something which serves as a rule or standard.

Another notable book acquired by John Flamsteed in exchange for one of his father's books on astrology was *Astronomia Carolina, or A New Theory of the Celestial Motions* by Thomas Street, published in London in 1661 and often referred to as the *Caroline Tables*.

This not only gave the positions of some of the brightest stars, the Moon and the planets but also enabled predictions of their future positions to be calculated. The ability to predict the places of the heavenly bodies in the sky was important both to those with an interest in the science of astronomy and to those who dabbled in astrology. For, if the astrologer could predict the future positions of stars and planets, he could advise his clients of the most auspicious moment in the future to initiate a certain action so as to achieve the desired purpose or objective. The astrologer who could determine future stellar and planetary positions would thus be able to use his knowledge to control future events, giving him a much greater sense of power and greater ability to manipulate his client. Astrology flourished in Western Europe during the 15th and 16th Centuries and even Johannes Kepler attempted to devise new methods of astrological computing which would be compatible with the change from an Earth-centred universe (the Ptolemaic system) to the Sun-centred astronomy of Copernicus. As we have previously noted, John Flamsteed was born at a time when astrological prognostications exerted a strong influence on people's minds and it was only slowly, with the wider understanding of Newtonian physics during the next 100 years or so, that astrology lost its power and was shown to be untenable as a true science. Armed with this acquisition of Street's *Astronomia Carolina* and his own knowledge of mathematics, Flamsteed set about predicting the future positions of the heavenly bodies, not for purposes of astrology but to show that the Sun, Moon and planets moved under the direction of scientific laws.

At the same time as the young John Flamsteed was utilising his leisure hours in the study of mathematics and astronomy, he was also involved in his father's business as a maltster and was coming into contact with several local gentlemen who also knew something about astronomy. One such gentleman was George Linacre, who impressed Flamsteed with his knowledge of the constellations and the positions of the fixed stars in the sky. Another was William Litchford, who had a good knowledge of the five "wandering stars" or planets which were then known (Mercury, Venus, Mars, Jupiter and Saturn) and had a small library of books on astronomy. Amongst these books was a work by the well-known contemporary astrologer John Gadbury and William Litchford told Flamsteed about a reliable set of astronomical tables compiled by Jeremiah Horrocks which was included in this particular volume. Although Flamsteed was anxious not to be dubbed an astrologer, he carefully studied the theories put forward by the astronomer and clergyman Horrocks and he became convinced that, for the motion of the Moon in particular, the ideas of Horrocks were far in advance of any other astronomer of the time. Jeremiah Horrocks (sometimes spelt in the Latinised form, Horrox) was born at Toxteth near Liverpool and after studying at Emmanuel College, Cambridge, was appointed curate at Hoole in Lancashire in 1639. Whilst there, when he was barely twenty years old, Horrocks predicted and made the first observation of the transit of the planet Venus across the face of the Sun. As this occurred on Sunday, December 4th he had to carry out the observation in between church services! He projected the Sun's image onto a white screen in a darkened room (as in a *camera obscura*) and measured the angular size of Venus as it crossed the image. He carried out other pioneering work in practical astronomy as well as performing theoretical studies. It was a great loss when Jeremiah Horrocks died suddenly in January 1641 at the early age of 23 years, leaving behind a great reputation as well as a good many written papers on astronomy which were later used by men such as John Flamsteed and Sir Isaac Newton. The prediction of the movement of the Moon against the background of the stars and planets in the night sky was one of the most difficult problems for mathematical astronomers of the 17th Century, but the lunar theory of Jeremiah Horrocks was commended by Newton as being the most ingenious and accurate of all explanations brought forward by contemporary mathematicians. He made use of Horrocks's work when writing his outstanding *Philosophiae Naturalis Principia Mathematica* of 1687.

As a gift for his friend William Litchford, John Flamsteed produced his first piece of written work on astronomy. This described the design, construction and use of the astronomer's quadrant, with associated tables for latitude 53 degrees, the latitude of their locality in Derbyshire. The completed work was entitled *Mathematical Essays* and Flamsteed, now just nineteen years old, presented it to his friend in August 1665.

Flamsteed's use of the *Caroline Tables* to predict the timing and extent of a partial solar eclipse which would be visible in Derbyshire early in the morning of June 22nd,1666, brought him to the attention of another local gentleman, Mr. Immanuel Halton. (This date was on the old style Julian calendar which was used in Britain until 1752. On our new style Gregorian calendar the eclipse took place on the 2nd of July, with its maximum at 6.41 a.m.). Immanuel Halton, who was nearly 20 years older than Flamsteed, lived a few miles north of Denby Village at Wingfield Manor - a stately home where the unfortunate Mary Queen of Scots had been held under house arrest around 1570. Halton also had a great interest in astronomy and possessed several books on the subject. Flamsteed made his prediction at the end of 1665 and his figures were available when he was visited by Mr. Halton just before Easter 1666. He was very impressed by Flamsteed's calculations of the eclipse and he promised to note the phenomenon carefully and compare the event with the prediction. Flamsteed also gave Immanuel Halton a copy of some mathematical tables entitled *A Canon of Natural and Artificial Versed Sines* which he had compiled and which might be useful to an astronomer.

Another eclipse of the Sun which was predicted by Flamsteed occurred around mid-day on the 25th of October 1668 (Julian calendar). He carefully observed this eclipse, using such primitive equipment as he then had and its details were published much later in the first volume of his *Historia Coelestis* - making this the earliest of his observations to appear in that famous catalogue of the heavens.

Later in the same year, Halton again visited Flamsteed at Derby and lent him a set of astronomical tables published in Latin in 1647 known as the *Richleian Tables*, composed by the Frenchman, Natalis Durret. Flamsteed read this publication carefully and compared it with his own observations. He was not very impressed by its accuracy, nor by the author's introduction, which he criticised and corrected in the margin before giving the book back to its owner. Flamsteed thought that these tables had been plagiarised from the *Rudolphine Tables* of Johannes Kepler. Already John Flamsteed was capable of assessing the work of other recent astronomers and was not afraid to criticise their writings, no matter how famous the authors, when their views failed to meet his observations.

CHAPTER III
A Visit to Southern Ireland

John Flamsteed's poor health continued to be a worry to his father, who could have wished for a more robust son to assist him in the family business and eventually to take over its management. But the young man was repeatedly affected by what he described as "a generalised weakness," which was often accompanied by "violent pains and shortness of breath." John Flamsteed himself must have been well aware of how his problematic health tended to reduce his capacity to contribute as much as would normally be expected by his family and he was always grateful for his father's understanding of his problem. He wrote a short account of his early life in which he mentions his appreciation of his father's sympathy at times when he was ill and of his father's efforts to try to find a cure for his sometimes prolonged and repeated bouts of ill-health. Also he expressed his thanks to God for the fact that his father was reasonably well-off and could afford to pay for all the medical treatments he had received, in the hope that someday he would find a cure.

Earlier he had been sent to Uttoxeter, in Staffordshire for convalescence and in an attempt to improve his health. Now, in the summer of 1665, the year of the Great Plague in London, it was decided that he should seek a cure in the south of Ireland, where a Mr. Valentine Greatrakes (or Greatorex) had achieved fame and acclamation as a notable healer who used the procedure known as "the laying on of hands" to heal many kinds of illness.

Amongst the many intelligent and educated people who had faith in Greatrakes' cures was, for instance, Robert Boyle, the scientist famous for his work on the properties of gases. He was born at Lismore in County Waterford near where Mr. Greatrakes held his practice and he firmly believed in this power of healing which Greatrakes exercised.

So, in an attempt to find a cure where orthodox medicine had failed, John Flamsteed set out on a journey to southern Ireland on the 26th of August, when he was 19 years and 6 days old, with the elderly family servant Clement Spicer as his companion. The journey involved crossing the Irish Sea and many miles of travel on difficult roads through wild countryside. Wisely they had planned to travel in late summer when the highways would be reasonably dry and more easily passable than during a wet Irish winter. Flamsteed kept a diary of his adventure, as he liked to record in a systematic manner the events of the day and the personalities he met. From this account it is possible to trace his route from Derbyshire all the way to the place where Mr. Greatrakes had his estate. This was known as the Assuane (or Affane) and was about 30 miles north-east of Cork and over 100 miles from Dublin.

The journey by road from Derby to Liverpool took the two men three days and then they had to wait a further three days until Friday, September 1st, for a boat and a suitable easterly wind to carry them across to Ireland. They embarked on a boat named the *Supply* and on the Saturday night they neared Dublin. Their boat was unable to reach harbour in Dublin that night due to a low tide and on the next day they were held up by regulations restricting the entry of people from England because of the severity of the London plague. The master of the boat went ashore to obtain landing permits for his passengers, but eventually they became impatient and restless and disembarked by means of a ladder let down onto the sands, walking ashore and eventually reaching a place known as King's End. After spending the night there, they set off to walk into Dublin and found lodgings at a hostelry, known as "The Ship", in Dame Street. Flamsteed and his companion stayed there for the next three days, making enquiries about the whereabouts of the celebrated Mr. Greatrakes, the best route to reach him, and hiring a horse to take them and their small amount of luggage on their way.

The first stage of their journey through Ireland took them to the small town of Naas (situated on the present-day N7 road) and to lodgings at Tomalins, some ten miles further on. From there, the next day they travelled on a route which probably lay along the present N9 road, though in the 17th Century this would have been only a cart track haphazardly connecting the villages and farmsteads which lay west of the Wicklow Mountains. They passed through the town of Carlow and the hamlet of Laughton Bridge (Leightinbridge) to Goaren (Gowran), Bennit's Bridge (Bennetsbridge) and finally to Barneschurch near Kilkenny, where they found overnight accommodation at another village inn. They had covered nearly forty miles that day and considering that John Flamsteed was not in the best of health, they must have been exhausted. They had only one horse between them, which would be loaded with their baggage and presumably one rode whilst the other had to walk much of the way.

The next day was Saturday and they pressed on, making every effort to reach their destination before the Sabbath - for in those days Sunday was a day for rest and church-going and they would most likely find great difficulty in obtaining refreshment and accommodation on that particular day. However, they were now in wild territory and progress became slower. They travelled on minor roads through Newton and Ballatoben to the larger town of Clonmel and then had to find an overnight resting-place at the village of Castleton.

On Sunday they continued their journey without attending church, as the villagers told them that for some considerable time they had been without a pastor to conduct services in the church, which was deserted. So they continued on their way, heading south through the Knockmealdown Mountains to Cappoquin on the River Blackwater. There was no bridge here, so they crossed the river by boat, leaving their horse behind and continuing on foot. It was not very far now to their destination at the Assuane - the place where they hoped to find the celebrated Valentine Greatrakes. They had been four days on the road from Dublin and were no doubt glad to be here at last - if only to be able to take a rest from the physical effort of constantly walking and riding. John Flamsteed, despite his bodily weakness, had not been too tired at the end of each day to make a brief record of the journey in his diary and now he must have been quite excited at the thought of meeting the famous healer about whom he had heard such good reports.

It was getting rather late in the day when they reached the Assuane, and it was also Sunday but they pressed on - heartened by the news that Mr. Greatrakes would still be working on the Sabbath. They finally made contact with him at his house and witnessed him curing several patients by the unusual and mysterious procedure known as "the laying on of hands." Arrangements were made for John Flamsteed to see him the following day.

On Monday morning, John and his companion met Mr. Greatrakes and the "laying on of hands" began. Because John was troubled chiefly by pains in his legs and swollen joints, these were the areas in which the healer concentrated his efforts. Unfortunately, at the end of the treatment session nothing seemed to have happened and the so-much-desired miraculous cure had not taken place. Nevertheless, it was thought worthwhile to repeat the treatment on the following morning.

So, early on Tuesday morning, John Flamsteed again presented himself for treatment at the house of Mr. Greatrakes and the healer began his work once more. This time the "laying on of hands" procedure took place over the whole of his body and was more thorough and extensive than during the first treatment. The result was no different however and there was still no cure. Mr. Greatrakes said that he would try again if John could come back in the afternoon. Accordingly, John returned for a third treatment. The outcome unfortunately was that again there was no improvement in his condition and both the healer and the patient had to admit that no cure seemed likely with that type of treatment. Flamsteed and his servant, Clement Spicer, decided to return home, disappointed that their hopes of a cure had proved fruitless. Although their time and their efforts in making the journey had been wasted, they parted in friendship from the celebrated Mr. Greatrakes.

The same afternoon they crossed the River Blackwater and

made the first twelve miles of their long journey back to Derbyshire. John was no doubt quite disappointed at the failure to find a cure and in rather low spirits. He noted in his diary that from Cappoquin the miles had been "long ones" and he was pleased to reach their lodgings at Clonmel that night.

The next day, Wednesday 13th September, saw the travellers on their homeward way again but early in the day their horse lost a shoe. They were delayed in looking around for a blacksmith and being unable to find one they had to continue their journey with the encumbrance of a stumbling horse. Having finally reached Goaren, they obtained accommodation for the night and managed to find a blacksmith's shop where the horse was re-shod.

During the next day, they retraced their outward route to Laughton Bridge, through Carlow and on to Kilcullen Bridge for a further overnight stay. They were now growing very weary of being constantly on the road but fortunately were only one day's journey from Dublin. On Friday the 15th of September, passing through Racoole (Rathcoole), they reached the city and secured accommodation again at "The Ship", their former lodging place, conveniently near the harbour.

The next stage of their journey was by sea, so having returned the horse to its owner they had to search around for a suitable ship. They found that the *Martin*, a boat from Liverpool, would be sailing back there on the following Tuesday and so they booked their passage on this vessel. The *Martin* left Dublin at 3 p.m. in the afternoon and came within sight of the Chester sand-bar on the following day. They entered the port of Liverpool soon after sunset and quickly disembarked, being anxious to secure their lodgings for the night - having spent the previous night out at sea.

The following day saw them again looking round for a horse and having obtained one they started on the journey south - arriving that evening at a place known as Zanchy Bridges (nowadays called Sankey Bridges, near Warrington, Cheshire). Two more wearisome days were to follow, as they made their way through Holmes Chapel to Congleton in Staffordshire and on the next day through Leek and Ashbourne to their home in Derby. They arrived after dark that night, no doubt completely exhausted by their travels. John Flamsteed does not record in his diary the response his father made to the disappointing news that the journey to Ireland had failed to provide the cure which they all had hoped for. He does mention, however, that on the day following their return, which was Sunday, he was unable to go to church because of the weariness brought on by his arduous journey and a further attack of the illness from which he suffered. It seems, according to the diary, that he would also have found it very difficult to sit down on a hard pew, due to the soreness of his lower regions brought on by so many days in the saddle!

The fact that Stephen Flamsteed encouraged his son to make this prolonged and difficult journey to southern Ireland shows how seriously he took the illness which John Flamsteed suffered from and how intensely they tried to find a cure. No ordinary physician seemed to be able to find a remedy and as people will do as a last resort, they turned in desperation and with great hope to alternative medicine.

The Irish visit was not the end of John Flamsteed's acquaintance with the famous Mr. Greatrakes. This celebrated healer announced that he would be visiting England in the early part of the New Year, 1666. Being still hopeful that a cure might be possible for his chronic health problem, John travelled to Worcester to meet Mr. Greatrakes again on February 12th, about five months after his trip to Ireland. A further session of healing was tried but again there was no improvement in his condition. Flamsteed was mystified as well as disappointed, because he had seen other patients apparently cured both in Ireland and at Worcester, whereas his own case was intractable.

The periodic bouts of illness which he had first experienced as a schoolboy, and which he hoped might have been cured in Ireland, continued to trouble Flamsteed. Nevertheless, he showed courage and a determination not to allow his health problem to interfere with his work or his objectives. His passionate interest in astronomy kept him mentally alert and his leisure time was always occupied in improving the quality of his observations. Whatever his illness might have been, it was not life-threatening and John Flamsteed lived to the age of 73 years - a ripe old age for any person in the 17th Century. He continued as a practical astronomer, observing and recording the stars, until only a few days before his death.

CHAPTER IV
Amateur Astronomy at Home

In the middle of the 17th Century, there was no one in Britain employed as a full-time professional astronomer, although the old-established Universities of Oxford and Edinburgh had Professors of Astronomy who taught the subject and also gave lectures in mathematics and other branches of science. At Gresham College, in London, Christopher Wren (1632-1723) was appointed Professor of Astronomy in 1657 during the Commonwealth period and in 1658 he and Robert Hooke (1635 - 1703) set up a telescope which was 36 feet long in the college grounds for their use in making astronomical observations. Hooke was appointed Professor of Geometry at Gresham College in 1665 and became actively engaged in many other sciences, notably physics and microscopy. He became "Curator of Experiments" for the Royal Society and performed demonstrations in front of the members at their weekly meetings held in Gresham College.

The "Royal Society of London for the Promotion of Natural Knowledge", to give it the full original title, was incorporated by charter from King Charles the Second in 1662, although it had existed as an informal collection of individuals who were "inquisitive into natural philosophy and other parts of human learning" since 1645. The members were mainly gentlemen of independent means who devoted part of their leisure time to various scientific pursuits and although some only dabbled in science in a desultory way others devoted themselves to a particular subject, becoming very knowledgeable as well as skilled practitioners. Such men were often called "virtuosi" because of their learning and skill and they were true amateurs in the sense that they loved their subject and devoted themselves to it - though they had no intention of making their living by that means.

John Flamsteed, by his early twenties, had become a very capable amateur astronomer. His initial interest had become fired by the study of the works of the ancient Greek and Arabian astronomers and by the more recent observations of Tycho Brahe, which had been made widely available in 1627 by Johannes Kepler in the *Rudolphine Tables*. These tables incorporated Tycho's pre-telescopic but none the less reasonably accurate, positional measurements of around one thousand stars and contained directions for locating the planets. The publication had been named in honour of Rudolph the Second, the Holy Roman Emperor who had been Kepler's patron and it contained the best data on the stars available, prior to John Flamsteed's own observations.

With the basic knowledge of mathematics he had obtained at school and from further private study at home, Flamsteed developed sufficient skill to be able to make rough predictions of the movement of the Moon. In particular, he was interested in the partial solar eclipse which was due on the 25th of October, 1668, when the Moon would partly cut off the light from the Sun in the daytime. He calculated tables for the commencement and duration of the eclipse and predicted the degree of obscuration it would produce over the Sun's disc. When the day came, he eagerly awaited the chance to test his calculations by actual observation - probably using the telescopic projection method described by Christopher Scheiner in 1630 for observing sunspots. The day, fortunately, was clear and the eclipse duly occurred, which might have given many individuals sufficient reason to feel great satisfaction with their work. But Flamsteed was a perfectionist who was less easily satisfied than other observers. He who had found fault in the fine detail of published work by other astronomers was now not entirely happy with the outcome of his own forecasts. In fact, he said that he was quite disappointed on the day to find that "the tables differed very much from the heavens." Only complete accuracy, within the experimental limits of his equipment, would have really pleased the young astronomer.

The fascination, however, of being able to carry out calculations regarding the movements of the Moon and planets across the sky and the degree of success which his early attempts had met with, made Flamsteed more determined than ever to continue with his hobby in the spare time he had available when released from his father's business. During 1669, he worked hard on the production of an Astronomical Almanac for 1670, basing this partly on the tables of earlier astronomers and partly on his own observations. He concentrated particularly on observing the progress of the planets Mars and Jupiter against the background of the fixed stars, using a telescope just 2 feet long. Flamsteed's almanac gave positions for the heavenly bodies and included a lunar eclipse, a possible solar eclipse and five appulses (close encounters) of the Moon with certain fixed stars. The proposed almanac was submitted to publishers but was rejected by them as being something far beyond the capacity of an unknown (and therefore, supposedly ignorant) member of the public. The detail of the work was probably its undoing, as it would have required the attention of a skilled astronomer to appreciate its value. Being in no way daunted by this rejection and possibly having learnt something from the publisher's response, Flamsteed then cut out the prediction of the eclipse and the appulses and decided to send an abbreviated version of his work for the consideration of the Royal Society.

The revised document was still quite lengthy but was now mainly a report on the eclipses of certain fixed stars by the Moon expected to occur during 1670, calculated from the *Caroline Tables* and corrected by means of his own observations. It was dated the 4th of November, 1669. Because of Flamsteed's diffidence in approaching such a distinguished body of gentlemen from his position as an unknown and unlettered amateur, he sent the document to the Royal Society by a rather roundabout route. Firstly it was sent to a Mr. John Stansby, who forwarded it to Mr. Elias Ashmole - a man of wide interests who, through his passion for astrology, knew a good deal about astronomy. (Ashmole later donated to Oxford University his valuable collection of natural curiosities and rarities, which became known as the Ashmolean Museum). Ashmole sent Flamsteed's communication forward to the President of the Royal Society, Lord Brouncker and it was presented at one of their weekly meetings in Gresham College.

The bashfulness with which Flamsteed, then only 23 years old, submitted his work to the Royal Society, was indicated by the way he signed his document *"In Mathesi a Sole fundes"* - an anagram of his name in the Latin form *Johannes Flamsteedius* - which might be translated "Go, You pour out learning from the Sun". The obvious scholarship of the author and the usefulness of his tables predicting the passage of the Moon through some of the brightest stars of the night sky, attracted the attention of several members of the Society. The work was immediately published in the *Philosophical Transactions of the Royal Society* as "An Accompt of such of the more notable Celestial Phaenomena of the year 1670, as will be conspicuous in the English Horizon..." After a few enquiries, the identity of this new and capable amateur astronomer was discovered and the Secretary, Mr. Henry Oldenburg, replied to Flamsteed on 14th January, 1670, thanking him for his communication and expressing the Society's interest in his work. Another member of the Society, Mr. John Collins, also wrote to Flamsteed on February 3rd and thus began a correspondence which was later to prove very much to Flamsteed's advantage.

John Flamsteed kept up a steady correspondence with Henry Oldenburg, giving him information on the procedures he intended to use for grinding and polishing lenses and asking in return for information on the reflector telescope which Isaac Newton had invented in 1668. Flamsteed firstly used fine sand as the cutting agent to grind his telescope lenses, then polished the surfaces using chalk and finally finished the lens using putty. He asked Oldenburg for details of any better methods or materials.

No doubt Stephen Flamsteed was a little surprised by the attention which these eminent London gentlemen paid to his son's correspondence and he must have been pleased that John, without any formal university training, had become such a capable astronomer as to attract their notice. Any deficiency in John's capabilities as far as the business in Derby was concerned, due to his indifferent health, was outweighed by the influential friends he was making amongst the educated gentlemen of London society. In 1672, Stephen Flamsteed was able to use one his son's friends in

London, John Collins, as his intermediary with London solicitors concerning the leasing of lead mines on the Derbyshire-Staffordshire border from the Duke of Albemarle - so his toleration of his son's interest in astronomy proved very useful on this occasion.

At around Easter 1670, John Flamsteed travelled to London to meet John Collins and Henry Oldenburg - those Fellows of the Royal Society who had found so much to interest them in the correspondence they had received from Derbyshire. They were impressed by his practical approach to astronomy, by his capabilities as shown in the document he had at first sent to them and by his obvious enthusiasm for the subject. Perhaps because Flamsteed's first letter had appeared in the Royal Society's *Philosophical Transactions* for January 1670 and had attracted widespread interest, John Collins took him to visit Jonas Moore who was the Surveyor-General of Ordnance at the Tower of London and who was knighted in 1673 for his services to the nation. Moore was a Lancastrian who had written several mathematical textbooks and had a great interest in astronomy. During the Civil War he had used the library of the antiquarian Christopher Towneley at Carr Hall in Pendle Forest, Lancashire, which contained some of the papers of the north-country astronomers Jeremiah Horrocks, William Crabtree and William Gascoigne, (and which John Flamsteed himself was later to visit). Sir Jonas Moore resided at the Tower of London because of his government role and his military connections. The Tower, at this time, was the headquarters of the Office of Ordnance and also functioned as a government centre for applied science, being well provided with technical people of all kinds, including carpenters, blacksmiths, gunsmiths and armourers.

The three counties of Yorkshire, Lancashire and Derbyshire had produced several capable amateur astronomers in the early 1600s. Of particular note had been the brilliant Jeremiah Horrocks who had predicted and carried out the first observation of the transit of Venus across the Sun's disc at Hoole in Lancashire in 1639. Then there was William Crabtree, who had corroborated Horrocks' observation of the transit from his home at Broughton, near Preston. Also there was William Gascoigne who had lived near York, and who had fought on the Royalist side in the Civil

War - tragically being killed at the battle of Marston Moor in 1644. He had written some excellent papers on optics, particularly describing the use of lenses in telescopes and the advantages of the Keplerian design. John Flamsteed afterwards made extensive use of Gascoigne's optical theory. William Gascoigne was also the first person to construct a finely pointed micrometer which could be fixed at the focal plane of an astronomical telescope to enable very small angles to be measured. This invention was to revolutionise the practice of astronomy in the hands of John Flamsteed.

Sir Jonas Moore was greatly impressed by Flamsteed and took this unknown young astronomer from Derbyshire under his wing. It was the patronage of Sir Jonas and the encouraging welcome he gave Flamsteed on this visit to London that was the turning point in Flamsteed's life. Before Flamsteed left, Sir Jonas presented him with lenses and a tube with which to construct a telescope and also gave him a micrometer so that he could measure angles and small objects in the telescope's field of view far more accurately than with his earlier home-made equipment. Also, Flamsteed gave John Collins three guineas so that he might obtain for him some further telescope lenses. These were received on 18th September, 1670, after he was back in Derby, but unfortunately he found that the eye-lenses did not suit his telescope. It was only in the autumn of 1671 that Flamsteed procured a better eye-piece and was able to make his 12-foot telescope operational. He continued to correspond with these friends in London and they did all in their power to encourage the young enthusiast.

On his journey home from London, Flamsteed made a detour to the University of Cambridge, where he entered his name as an undergraduate at Jesus College. In Cambridge he met some of the most eminent scientists of the time. Dr. Isaac Barrow (1630-1677) had been Professor of Geometry at Gresham College in London, before being appointed to the newly-created Lucasian Chair of Mathematics in Cambridge in 1663. He resigned from this Professorship in 1669 in favour of Isaac Newton - who had been his pupil. Isaac Newton, that outstanding genius who invented the calculus, was already a professor of some distinction at the age of 27 years when Flamsteed visited Cambridge as a 23 year old intended undergraduate. There was little difference in their actual ages but Newton was already an established academic and perhaps this early superiority of Newton underlay the personal conflicts which later ensued between them. Another Cambridge scholar, who took an interest in astronomy and became a good friend of John Flamsteed, was Dr. Richard Wroe - a Fellow of Jesus College. They maintained a regular correspondence for the next four years.

It appears that John Flamsteed never took up full residence in Cambridge. He was there for two months, however, in 1674, during which time he probably attended Newton's Lucasian Lectures. At this period of his life, he still continued to assist his father, whilst pursuing his own astronomical work and such mathematical studies as interested him, from his home in Derbyshire.

In June 1670, soon after his return from London, Flamsteed visited Lancashire on behalf of his father's business and called to see Mr. Richard Towneley, the nephew of Christopher Towneley, in whose library were the papers of the deceased astronomers, Horrocks, Crabtree and Gascoigne, about which Sir Jonas Moore had informed Flamsteed. The Towneleys were Roman Catholic gentry who employed a servant to help in their astronomical observations and although Richard Towneley was not at home when Flamsteed called, the servant showed him the library and their telescopes and how to fit a micrometer to a telescope. This visit to Lancashire was, therefore, a very useful one as far as John Flamsteed was concerned and he proceeded to form a close friendship with Richard Towneley which lasted for many years. In 1672, after Flamsteed had predicted that the planet Mars would appear inside a group of three small stars in the constellation Aquarius, he visited Towneley Hall again and together they looked for the expected event. They used Towneley's equipment and found that Flamsteed's calculations agreed exactly with the position of Mars in the sky – no doubt to Flamsteed's great satisfaction. Towneley also showed Flamsteed a "weather glass" or mercury barometer which he owned, made after the pattern described by the Italian inventor Toricelli in 1643 and he told Flamsteed about the rules he had devised for predicting the weather. After returning home, Flamsteed made himself a barometer and carefully read the glass three times a day for the next three years – linking the rise or fall of the mercury to the changes he noted in the weather.

Another instrument made by Flamsteed for his own observations linked to the weather was a "tinged spirit thermometer" - a device invented in 1641 by Ferdinand, Duke of Burgundy. The correspondence between Towneley and Flamsteed henceforth contained many references to the subject of forecasting the weather.

The micrometer, which Sir Jonas Moore had given to Flamsteed and which had been fitted at the principal focus of his telescope, made a huge difference to the observations he could now make. He measured the visual diameters of the planets and showed that this varied with their distance from the Earth. These observations, probably improved by more accurate work done later at Greenwich, were given to Isaac Newton, who made use of them when he wrote the fourth book of his *Principia*.

Flamsteed also used the micrometer to measure the small changes which occur in the apparent diameter of the Sun and the Moon as their distance from Earth varies, due to the eccentricity of the orbits involved. He also noted carefully the movements of the four visible satellites of Jupiter and measured their greatest elongations in terms of the planet's diameter. At the invitation of the Royal Society Flamsteed corresponded with the famous Italian astronomer Giovanni Domenico Cassini, who had been appointed Director of the Paris Observatory in 1671. Cassini was an excellent observer who had some superb telescopes. He found that Jupiter was not a true sphere but was slightly flattened at the poles. Flamsteed at first denied this but after further careful measurements with his micrometer he had to admit that Cassini was right.

The most remarkable measurements that Flamsteed carried out at this period were his estimations of the Sun's parallax, that is, the change in angle of the Sun against the background of fixed stars from morning to evening on any given day. He found that this was "not more than 10 seconds of arc" - a very small angle to measure using the equipment he had available and the method he employed (see Chapter 9). A modern value for the solar parallax is 8.8 seconds of arc.

At the same time, Flamsteed continued with his mathematical predictions of the positions of the Moon and the planets relative to the fixed stars. He would regularly forward these calculations to Henry Oldenburg, the Secretary of the Royal Society, who would then print them in the Society's *Philosophical Transactions*. By this stage of his life, Flamsteed had become quite certain that the heavenly bodies moved in accordance with mathematical rules and their future positions could be accurately predicted if one could only work out these rules. The subject of Astrology no longer had any attraction for him and he wrote a forthright and controversial article saying how useless was this study and how ignorant of true science were those who practised it. The article was received with approval amongst the clergymen of his acquaintance but because astrological predictions were popular with the general public it did not circulate as widely as Flamsteed would have liked. On another occasion, when his cousin Mr. Thomas Willson of Codnor (a village some two miles from Denby Village) was due to visit Henry Oldenburg and John Collins in London, he urged him to put forward a strong plea for more attention to be given to true scientific astronomy rather than worthless astrological fancies. "Pray in your discourses with these gentlemen informe them that I am vext to see our Ephemeredists spend the pages of their Almanacks in Astrologicall whimseys, tendeing onely to abuse the people and disturbe the publique with anxious and jealous praedictions, whilest the praemonition of Coelestiall appearances which ought to be theire onely charge is wholly contemned or neglected."

Flamsteed continued to correspond with Sir Jonas Moore, sending him a table of the Moon's rising and setting throughout 1674 and also the eclipses and close encounters of the Moon and planets to certain fixed stars that should be expected. Sir Jonas found that Flamsteed's table of the Moon gave him a means of closely estimating the state of the tides, which was quite important along the tidal stretch of the River Thames in London and which he could easily observe from his home at the Tower.

Flamsteed also provided Sir Jonas with two barometric "weather glasses" and the materials for making more. These were passed on to King Charles, who kept one for himself and gave the other to his brother, James, the Duke of York. Both these members of the Royal Family were interested in science and had been shown telescopes and micrometers used for astronomical observations and they were now very impressed by these new scientific instruments. They developed a high opinion of John Flamsteed because of these gifts and Sir Jonas Moore's portrayal of his excellent capabilities.

In the summer of 1674, again on his way to Cambridge, Flamsteed visited Sir Jonas Moore in London and discussed their mutual interests. Sir Jonas thanked Flamsteed for his Moon table and remarked how closely the phases of the Moon had corresponded with the tides on the River Thames. He suggested that King Charles would probably appreciate having an accurate tide table for the year 1675 and offered to provide an assistant to help with such a task, which would involve lengthy calculations. This tide table, specifically for the Thames at London Bridge, was completed by John Flamsteed just prior to Christmas 1674 and, together with a further edition of his *Equation of Time* (which corrected for differences between time as shown by a sun-dial and that indicated by a pendulum clock), was presented to the king under the title *The Royal Almanack*. It should be noted that all this took place long before Newton's theory of gravity had been circulated and Flamsteed's work was based on experience and empirical formulae rather than a comprehensive understanding of how the tides were caused.

Thanks to Sir Jonas Moore's patronage and contact with the king, John Flamsteed was granted the degree of Master of Arts of the University of Cambridge *per literatus regius*. The warrant from King Charles II, issued on June 5th, 1674, instructed the university "to grant an MA degree to John Flamsteed, late of Jesus College, who has spent many years in the study of the liberal arts and sciences, especially of astronomy, in which he has already made such useful observations as are well esteemed by persons eminently learned in that science."

Having attained his degree without having to satisfy the usual residence requirement, Flamsteed returned to Derby. The equipment he now possessed included a 13-foot telescope and a shorter 7-foot one together with a micrometer. He had also constructed a wooden quadrant of 3-foot radius in order accurately to measure angles greater than could be seen in the field of his telescope. He calibrated the micrometer by setting up a carefully marked rod with intervals of 1, 3, 6, 36, 72 and 108 inches clearly marked, at a distance of 908 ft 7 inches from the 13-foot telescope. Flamsteed claimed that he could measure angles to an accuracy of 5 seconds of arc with this equipment and because he was a very painstaking observer, who always paid careful attention to experimental accuracy, he might well have been right.

The accurate measurement of time took a great step forward in the middle of the 17th Century and Flamsteed was aware that a good pendulum-controlled clock would be of immense value in his observations. The Dutch physicist and astronomer Christiaan Huygens (1629-1695) invented the pendulum clock in 1656 and these clocks generally had a short pendulum and were designed to hang on a wall. There were very few of these in Derbyshire in the 1670s and they were very expensive. Clocks with a long pendulum which swung once every second were introduced by the English clock-maker William Clement in 1670 and this brought in the era of the "grandfather clock" but at this early period of Flamsteed's life such clocks were extremely rare in this country. John Flamsteed regretted that his father would not obtain such a clock to help with his observations.

At the age of nearly 28 years, John Flamsteed had his recent M.A. degree and a great interest in astronomy but he had no profession (other than as an assistant in his father's business enterprises). He was considering being ordained in the Anglican Church and seeking a small living as a country parson somewhere near his home in Derby. He planned to be ordained at Peterborough Cathedral at Christmas 1674 and in fact travelled as far as Oakham in the county of Rutland with this in view. However, he stopped and returned home after being told that no ordinations were taking place at Peterborough at that time. He finally took holy orders at Ely House (in London) under Bishop Gunning at Easter 1675 and might easily have passed into relative obscurity as a country parson who dabbled in astronomy. But fate intervened and Flamsteed's appointment to a position as an Anglican clergyman was delayed for many years.

CHAPTER V

Founding the Royal Observatory at Greenwich

John Flamsteed's ability in astronomy and science had been noticed by Sir Jonas Moore from the very first time he had met him, when John Collins had introduced him on his first visit to the Tower of London in 1670. Sir Jonas had kept in touch with him throughout the next few years and after Flamsteed had been granted his Cambridge degree, with no further particular involvement in science in view, perhaps Sir Jonas was inclined to think that his talents would be wasted as a Derbyshire clergyman. Also, Sir Jonas was searching for a suitable associate for his son, who he hoped would eventually succeed him at the Office of Ordnance and he required someone with enthusiasm and ability to impart a knowledge of mathematics and astronomy to this young man. In February 1675, therefore, Flamsteed was invited to visit Sir Jonas at the Tower once again, to see if he might be interested in becoming an assistant to his son and heir. However, this arrangement proved fruitless when it was found that Flamsteed failed to get on well with the son on account of the young man's temperament, so Sir Jonas realised that his intention would not be a practical proposition. Notwithstanding this failure in his plan, Sir Jonas obviously liked John Flamsteed and he asked him to stay on at the Tower for a while and carry out some astronomy whilst he was there. Flamsteed was provided with the equipment he needed and given facilities for observing from a turret of the White Tower. He was also shown the capabilities which the Tower possessed as a centre for applied science and technology.

A great national concern at this time was the question of how to determine the longitude (the east-west position) of a ship at sea. Exploration of the Atlantic coast of North America and amongst the islands of the West Indies had been steadily increasing during the past 100 years and there were already several British settlements of important commercial interest situated there. In navigating to such places, it was vital to know the position of a ship at sea. The north-south position was fairly easily determined by noting the vertical angle (or altitude) of the Sun at its maximum elevation or the angle of the Pole Star. But estimations of the east-west longitude could sometimes be in error by 200 miles or more. (The solution to the problem of finding the longitude at sea became later, in 1714, the subject of a prize of £20,000 offered by the government).

In February 1675, Sir Jonas Moore took Flamsteed to see King Charles (figure 3) and during their conversation the notable achievements of the French in astronomy and navigation were described. The King of France had appointed G-D Cassini as Director of the Paris Observatory following its completion in 1671, and perhaps King Charles concluded that Britain was lagging behind in this vital work of such practical commercial and military importance.

One who claimed to have found a method for determining the longitude from the altitude of two stars and the position of the moon was a Frenchman, known as Le Sieur de St. Pierre, who had influence at the English Court through a young Breton lady, Louise de Keroualle (1649-1734). This very attractive girl had been lady-in-waiting to the Duchess of Orleans in France and was brought to England to serve as maid-of-honour to Queen Catherine but she had soon taken King Charles' eye and had become another of the king's mistresses. The king elevated her to the rank of Duchess of Portsmouth in 1673 after she had borne him a son and she was afterwards regarded as the king's principal mistress. St. Pierre used her proximity to the king to bring his claim to have "discovered the longitude" to royal attention. This assertion greatly interested the king and he immediately appointed a Commission to look into the Frenchman's claim. Sir Jonas Moore

Figure 3.
King Charles II, who had the Royal Observatory built
at Greenwich in 1675.
By courtesy of the National Portrait Gallery, London.

was a member of this Commission, which also included Lord
Brouncker (President of the Royal Society), Dr. Seth Ward (a
former Professor of Astronomy at Oxford and now Bishop of
Salisbury), Sir Christopher Wren (the former Professor of
Astronomy at Gresham College and at Oxford), Sir Charles
Scarborough, Colonel Silius Titus, Dr. John Pell, Sir Samuel
Morland and Robert Hooke. This distinguished body of men, at

the suggestion of Sir Jonas Moore and because they knew of his capabilities as a practical astronomer, asked John Flamsteed to become advisor to the Commission. St. Pierre had claimed that he could calculate the longitude of any locality if he were given the date and certain astronomical information. He required the altitude of two stars and knowledge of which side of the meridian they appeared, the height of the Moon's upper and lower limbs and the height of the Pole star - all the data to be in degrees and minutes of arc. The Commission asked Flamsteed to supply this information for a test on St. Pierre's method.

John Flamsteed produced the requisite data within a few days, giving it to Dr. Pell (who probably acted as secretary to the Commission) on the 19th of February, 1675. At the same time, Flamsteed also sent his written critical comments on the method for determining the longitude which St. Pierre had indicated, which he said would not give satisfactory results. Although the method might work in theory, Flamsteed declared, the basic astronomical information was not known to a sufficient degree of accuracy at that time. The best available star catalogue, based on the naked-eye observations of Tycho Brahe, would be far too inaccurate and the position calculated might be in error by a hundred or more miles. Flamsteed suggested that to gather all the necessary data on the stars would take many years of observation with large and well-calibrated telescopes. This was later proved to be a true comment and the search for the accurate positional information which this method for the determination of longitude depended on was to occupy astronomers the world over for the next 150 years.

King Charles was informed that St. Pierre had been given the data to test his method but that Flamsteed was sceptical about his success due to the lack of precise astronomical tables. The king was surprised that the best information on star positions they then had was so poor, and he determined to do all that he could to remedy the situation and provide accurate navigational charts for the use of his seamen. He decided that an observatory should be built as soon as possible in one of the Royal Parks and that the necessary observations should be made so that the positions of the stars, Sun, Moon and planets might be sufficiently well determined. Furthermore, due to Sir Jonas Moore's influence, John Flamsteed was appointed by Royal Warrant to be the king's "Astronomical Observator" with an official salary to support his work. The job description was that he should "forthwith apply himself with the most exact care and diligence to the rectifying of the tables of motion of the heavens, and the places of the fixed stars, so as to find the so-much-desired longitude of places for the perfecting of the art of navigation." The royal warrant was conveyed to John Flamsteed on March 4th, 1675, by Sir Jonas Moore. Flamsteed was 28 years old at this time and his appointment as "astronomical observator" was to occupy him for the next 44 years.

On hearing information concerning Flamsteed's appointment, St. Pierre was very upset and again sought to gain the ear of King Charles. He realised that the calculations he had made, based on the information provided by the Royal Commission, had not given the correct answer and he now claimed that the information he had been provided with had been "feigned." Because he spoke very little English he protested in Latin that the information given him had been fictitious and ridiculous, relating as it did to the year 1673. Could he have some further data for the present year, 1675? Through Louise de Keroualle, Duchess of Portsmouth, the Frenchman continued to worry the king and so, to prevent further hassle, King Charles requested his Commission to supply more information or to silence St. Pierre some other way. Flamsteed immediately replied with reports written in English for the king and the Royal Commission and another in Latin for St. Pierre. He said that the method St. Pierre was using had been described many years before by Christian Longomontanus (a Dutch associate of Tycho Brahe) and by Jean-Baptiste Morin, a French astronomer. In fact, the idea of determining longitude by this method had originated with Johannes Werner of Nuremberg (1468-1522) and was called the lunar-distance method. It took more than 250 years from Werner's theoretical description of the method for it to become a practical reality with the publication in the 1760s of the *Nautical Almanac*. Flamsteed advised St. Pierre to study more closely the work of his countryman (known by the Latin form of his name as Morinus) before he made any more claims to be able to determine the longitude. The final outcome was that, in Flamsteed's words, "He huffed a little and disappeared, since which time we have heard no further of him".

The salary deemed appropriate for the post of king's astronomer was fixed at £100 per year, payable by the Board of Ordnance. Flamsteed was disappointed by this rather meagre salary, out of which he had to pay £10 income tax and from which he had to pay any assistant he might require as well as the cost of any astronomical instruments. As things turned out, his salary was often delayed and paid very late, leaving him with a serious shortage of funds. We must remember, however, that at this time astronomy was usually carried out by gentlemen of private means, who did not depend upon it as a regular source of income. Flamsteed was the first person in Britain to receive a government salary for his practical work in astronomy and the concept of such a post was quite new in this country. His salary was perhaps intended merely to supplement another income and it was probably thought that he would continue to receive money from his father's business, or that as a pious churchman he would gain the living of some convenient country parish to boost his finances. However, Flamsteed was principally interested in astronomy and he struggled along in difficult financial straits during these early years. It was only some 10 years later, in 1684, when finally forced into it by the poverty of his position as the king's astronomer, that he accepted an appointment in the Anglican Church.

The most suitable site for the Royal Observatory was debated and several places were suggested. One proposal was for Hyde Park, favoured by Sir Jonas Moore. Flamsteed, on the other hand, would have preferred the site of Chelsea College, then in ruins, because it was near the court of King Charles. Sir Christopher Wren suggested the site of Greenwich Castle in Greenwich Park which was on high ground, visible from a long stretch of the River Thames and away from the smoke of London's most built-up areas. It was important that the site of the observatory should be in a Royal Park so that no land had to be purchased, as the money available was insufficient to pay for anything more than the basic building. Wren's suggestion was quickly agreed to, as the old Greenwich Castle (a Parliamentary garrison during the Civil War) had been demolished in the 1660s and its foundations could be re-used to save costs. Greenwich Castle had originally been built as a hunting-tower in the park by Humphrey, Duke of Gloucester, in the 1430s. It had been substantially renovated by King Henry VIII in 1526, when the park had been used for jousting tournaments and other militaristic pursuits. In the reign of Queen Elizabeth I, it was called "Mirefleur" but was given the name Greenwich Castle when it was occupied by the forces of Parliament during the Civil War. After the Restoration, Charles II had the tower pulled down, perhaps on account of its recent use by an anti-royalist garrison but in any case, the original building must have been rather dilapidated after more than 200 years.

Flamsteed thought it a great pity that the foundations of the old castle were to be used again in the construction of the observatory, as its walls were 13.5 degrees away from a true north-south alignment, thus making the fixing of observational quadrants on the walls and the use of a telescope in the meridian pointing at right angles out of a window very awkward. However, the budget for the project was clearly stated in the king's warrant of 22nd June, 1675; "the total sum to be expended and paid shall not exceed £500". Because of the need for economy in the construction, some wood, iron and lead from a recently demolished gatehouse at the Tower of London were used together with bricks from Tilbury Fort. Some of the cost was covered by money obtained from the sale of 690 barrels of old and decayed gunpowder. So, with the greatest care and the use of these second-hand materials the observatory was eventually completed at a cost of £520. 9s. 1d.

The site of the Royal Observatory at Greenwich stands high on the south side of the Thames, overlooking the elegant "Queen's House", which was designed by Inigo Jones (see figure 4). The building of this royal house, where John Flamsteed stayed for some weeks whilst the observatory was being built, commenced in 1616 for Anne of Denmark who was consort to King James I and was completed around 1638 for Henrietta Maria, the French wife of their son, the ill-fated King Charles I. In comparison with the £500 allocated for the observatory, the intended budget for the Queen's House was in excess of £4000.

The design of the Royal Observatory "for the observator's

habitation and a little for pompe" was by Sir Christopher Wren, who, after a distinguished career as an astronomy professor, had been appointed Surveyor of Works by the king in 1669. Wren was very much involved with the rebuilding work which followed the Great Fire of London in 1666 and is, of course, best remembered as the architect of St. Paul's Cathedral. He was assisted in his surveying work by Robert Hooke, a man of many talents, who also was involved in the building of the observatory. Indeed, Hooke may have made a large contribution to the observatory's overall design.

Figure 4.
View of the Royal Observatory looking towards the north, showing the Queen's House and the River Thames below Greenwich Hill. The sextant and quadrant house, where Flamsteed carried out his most accurate observations, is the flat-topped building on the extreme right of this picture. The tall mast supported a 60 foot long telescope.
By courtesy of the National Maritime Museum, London.

In July 1675, John Flamsteed moved from the Tower of London to Greenwich, so that he also could keep an eye on the work as it progressed. The building work started on the 10th of August and proceeded rapidly, with the roof being finished before Christmas - only four months later. Flamsteed was accommodated at the

Queen's House and was allocated a place there to keep his telescopes and the 3 ft quadrant he had brought down from Derby. He made observations from the Long Gallery at the Queen's House during October and November 1675, including some of the Moon, and also measured the height of the observatory above low water-level in the River Thames, which he calculated was 182 feet.

Whilst Flamsteed was at the Tower of London, he designed an astronomical sextant of 6 feet 9 inches radius (See Appendix 1, C and figures 18 and 19) which Sir Jonas Moore caused to be constructed, at first in wood and later in iron, by the Master Smith at the Tower, Edward Sylvester. A brass radial limb, half an inch thick, was fitted to the sextant and this carried brackets for the attachment of a telescope. The alignment of the telescope could be finely adjusted by means of a calibrated screw wheel which engaged with gear teeth on the limb but Flamsteed also took the precaution of leaving room for small radial angles to be inscribed around the circumference of the instrument. The sextant was calibrated using a carefully marked rail set up at a distance of 8762 inches (about 243 yards) at one end of a flat terrace alongside the river. The rail was divided into minutes of arc and also 10 second intervals (10 seconds of arc was equivalent to 0.422 inches on the rail). Although the Tower workmen were not used to precision engineering, Flamsteed was satisfied that the sextant "worked well enough". Thomas Tompion, England's finest clockmaker at that time, performed the accurate wheel-work and inscribed the scales on the sextant. When in use, the sextant required three operators. One, (the senior observer), manned the moveable telescope and aligned this with the right-hand object; the second observer kept the fixed telescope aligned on the left-hand object; whilst the third man needed to be strong and able-bodied to manipulate the heavy instrument in the plane of the observation. After the sextant came into regular use at the observatory, on 19th September 1676, Flamsteed was pleased to find that he could observe the planet Venus in daylight within 16 degrees of the Sun, whereas Tycho and the Polish astronomer Hevelius could not see this planet using their naked-eye instruments at less than 40 degrees from the Sun.

With the Towneley micrometer that Sir Jonas Moore had given him, fitted to a 13 feet 9 inches long telescope, Flamsteed claimed that he could measure angles as small as 5 seconds of arc. His calibration of the micrometer had been carried out in Derbyshire, using a marked rod set up at a distance of 908 feet 7 inches from the telescope, so that a 1 inch division would correspond to 18.91 seconds of arc.

Flamsteed also requested a large Mural Arc, or calibrated semicircle, for the observatory but Sir Jonas Moore, having spent more than he expected on the iron sextant, declined to fund this. Instead, Robert Hooke offered to make a 10 foot radius quadrant (See Appendix 1, B and figure 16) at a smaller cost, and this was agreed. Flamsteed did not see this instrument until it was completed and despite its simple elegant appearance he was very disappointed at the poor quality of its workmanship and its general awkwardness in use. It was fixed onto a strong wall running north-south so that vertical angles in the meridian could be measured. This mural arc made by Hooke was also found to be dangerous to use: Flamsteed declaring, "I tore my hands on it, and it had like to have deprived Cuthbert of his fingers". Cuthbert Denton was one of Flamsteed's early assistants at Greenwich and presumably the radial arm to which the telescope was attached could swing downwards if not secured and trap or cut the hand of the operator between the frame and the arm. This quadrant was used until September 1680 but it was never a success.

To achieve accurate measurements of time, Sir Jonas Moore ordered two "Great Clocks" from the best clock-maker in England, Thomas Tompion (1638 - 1713) and gave these as his personal gift to John Flamsteed. These clocks (see figure 5) were designed to run for a whole year without winding and had 13-foot long pendulums which beat every two seconds fitted above the clock faces. Their faces bore the inscription "Motus Annuus" (yearly movement) and "Sir Jonas Moore caused this movement with great care to be thus made in the year 1676 by Thomas Tompion". The two clocks were similar, except that the pendulum for one pivoted on a knife-edge whilst the other was suspended by means of a piece of springy metal. Sir Christopher Wren made the ceiling of the main observation room, known as the Octagon Room, 20 feet high so that these clocks could be accommodated. The height of this room was also useful, of course, when long telescopes, which were the norm in those days, were to be pointed out of the long vertical windows. The pin-wheel escapements of the Great Clocks were made according to a pattern described by Richard Towneley, the friend of Flamsteed and of Sir Jonas Moore and Tompion blamed this type of escapement for some of the problems they later experienced with the clocks. Flamsteed (perhaps more

Figure 5.
The face of one of the Tompion "Great Clocks", 1676.

correctly) gave other reasons - temperature variations affecting the pendulum length, dust or swarf in the mechanism, strong winds shaking the building, the clock hands sticking, or a lack of oil in the movements. Flamsteed was a meticulous experimenter who had a careful eye for detail and he kept a close check on each clock against the other in order that he could time his observations of the stars to a second.

The elegant Octagon Room, situated above the four living rooms which Flamsteed occupied, commanded a great view of the sky from its windows and with its ornate ceiling and wood-panelled walls and life-size portraits of King Charles and the Duke of York above the clock faces, was the room in which to entertain important visitors. Much of Flamsteed's work, however, was carried out in a small building in the garden, known as the sextant

Figure 6.
The Octagon Room at the Royal Observatory.
This was the most magnificent room in the building, with facilities for using long astronomical telescopes.
It also contained the Tompion "Great Clocks" and portraits of King Charles II and his brother, the Duke of York.
By courtesy of the National Maritime Museum, London.

and quadrant house (see figure 7). This was roughly built of brick-work, with a timber roof which could be drawn back when observing was due to commence. This building also had the special wall which ran truly north-south to support Hooke's quadrant and later the mural arc. It defined Flamsteed's meridian from 1676 and was the site where his most accurate observations were made. This led eventually to international acceptance in 1884 of the Greenwich meridian as the world standard reference of longitude, which has been used since then for all scientific and navigational purposes.

John Flamsteed moved into full occupation of the Royal Observatory on its completion on July 10th, 1676, three days after the installation of the "Great Clocks" in the Octagon Room and he was to live there for the next 43 years. The dedicatory inscription, written in Latin on an ornate stone plaque built into the wall of what came to be known as "Flamsteed House" is translated: "The most excellent King Charles the Second, greatest patron of the Arts of Astronomy and Navigation, had this Observatory built to serve both Arts in the year of our Lord 1676, in the 28th year of his reign. By the care of Jonas Moore, Knight, Surveyor General of the Ordnance."

Chapter VI

Starting Work at the Greenwich Observatory

O n moving into the Royal Observatory at Greenwich, John Flamsteed was well aware of the magnitude of the task that lay before him and the practical importance of the work he had to do relating to both astronomy and navigation. Also he no doubt realised that the eyes of King Charles and the eminent Fellows of the Royal Society in London, as well as other notable astronomers overseas such as Cassini in Paris and Hevelius in Danzig, would be focused upon his work. He was now 29 years old, unmarried and a stranger in London except for the acquaintance of Sir Jonas Moore and a few other scientific friends. He wrote at this time concerning the rather daunting prospect of his role as the Astronomer Royal, "May the great Author of the Universe, the all-wise Disposer of the Heavenly Bodies, assist me in this undertaking. May he grant me health and leisure to accomplish it, and render my ideas of His Works agreeable to the Prototype: that mankind may have the use, and He the glory of my labours".

A great mistake made by the king and his commissioners from the outset was that the Royal Astronomer was expected to provide his own equipment and necessary instruments from his own meagre salary and this led to serious problems later on. Flamsteed had no private income and had reached his present eminent position in astronomy on very limited resources. Fortunately, he had the telescopes and the quadrant he had brought from Derby and which were now stored in the Queen's House and these were easily carried up the hill to the observatory. Also, he had the magnificent 6 foot 9 inches radius sextant which had been made at the Tower and generously given him by Sir Jonas Moore. The large and cumbersome Mural Quadrant, made by Robert Hooke, was also available but although this was used to measure the angle of stars above the horizon until September 1680, it was never a complete success and Flamsteed never really trusted the readings he obtained with it. Fortunately, he possessed two excellent state-of-the-art clocks which Sir Jonas had also given him.

The Office of the Ordnance provided Flamsteed with the help of an assistant from the Tower to carry equipment around, read the clock when required, wake the astronomer at appropriate times during the night and assist with the heavy sextant. Flamsteed complained that this man was "a surly silly labourer" and a hindrance rather than a help, who would wander away and waste a lot of his time in eating (or more probably drinking) in various Greenwich hostelries. In 1694, however, the Office of Ordnance allowed Flamsteed to choose his own assistant and he was then able to employ "an ingenious and tractable youth" instead of a rude labourer. As the sextant needed three people to operate it, Flamsteed had to pay for another assistant, who could be trained to take on a more technical role, from his own salary. The sextant needed some preparatory work in setting up, assessing its experimental errors, and in calibration before it could be used for accurate observations and it was first used for real measurements on 19th September, 1676. The assistants who moved to the observatory with Flamsteed were Cuthbert Denton (the surly labourer) and Thomas Smith, who filled the more technical post.

One of the first projects which Flamsteed set himself was to measure the latitude (the north-south position) of Greenwich. He did this by carefully measuring the angle of the Pole Star from the zenith (the vertical above the observer's head). In 1677, he determined this latitude as 51 degrees 28 minutes 50 seconds North but corrected it for atmospheric refraction to 51 degrees 28 minutes 10 seconds. Further measurements on the position of stars in the constellation Ursa Major, taken with his 7ft radius Sextant, gave Greenwich a latitude of 51 degrees 29 minutes 22 seconds, corrected for refraction to 51 degrees 28 minutes 30 seconds. Later, towards the end of 1689, Flamsteed again repeated this measurement using the Mural Arc and obtained the latitude of Greenwich as 51 degrees 28 minutes 34 seconds. This compares with the accepted modern measurement of 51 degrees 28 minutes 38 seconds.

Another project that Flamsteed embarked upon was to observe the rotation of the Earth relative to the fixed stars and thus to prove that it rotates at constant speed. This was one of the reasons he had acquired the two Great Clocks which could keep running accurately for more than a year without winding. It was a fundamental necessity to be sure of this constant rotational speed in order that observations of the heavenly bodies could be linked to time measurements and consequently for astronomical observations to be used for accurate navigational purposes. In 1677, Flamsteed had managed to keep his daily observations and his clocks going for three months without interruption or breakdown and he wrote to his friend Richard Towneley that his measurements so far confirmed the assumption that the Earth's rotational speed was constant. However he needed nine months further continuous observations to prove his point and the clocks had to run reliably throughout this period with little or no attention. The poverty in which he lived was also beginning to take its toll and he told Towneley that he himself might starve inside that time limit as his salary was too small and already he was nine months in arrears with his pay. He wrote, "I feare I must come downe into the country to seeke some poor vicarage, and then farewell to our [crucial] experiment".

Fortunately Flamsteed persevered through this period of adversity and eventually, in 1678, he was able to write to his patron Sir Jonas Moore informing him that he had now proved that the Earth rotates on its axis at a constant rate and also that his "Equation of Natural Days" (or Equation of Time) had been verified. Sir Jonas would no doubt be very pleased that the two clocks he had given to his young friend had been put to such good use. Flamsteed's result was to stand without challenge for the next 250 years, though nowadays it is known that the rotation of the Earth is gradually slowing down due to the friction of the tides.

Also, there are other small irregularities which have been shown by the use of modern Caesium Atomic Clocks. Generally speaking though, these irregularities can be ignored in all but the most accurate measurements of time.

Another great question Flamsteed sought to answer was, "How far away are the stars?" He knew that the stars were at such large distances that to an observer on Earth they appeared to be fixed in position. But could he find their distance by careful experiment? A rather bizarre piece of equipment at the new observatory was designed to try to answer this question; it was known as the "Well Telescope" and could only scan a small area of sky directly overhead. The idea was to measure the parallax, or change in angle, of the second magnitude star Gamma Draconis, at times when the Earth was at opposite ends of its orbit around the Sun, that is at intervals of six months. Using the diameter of the Earth's orbit as baseline, triangulation would give the distance to the star.

Figure 7.
The southern side of the Royal Observatory, 1676, showing the tall mast for raising Flamsteed's 60 foot telescope.
The Sextant and Quadrant House can be seen in the corner of the site in front of the main observatory building and the top of the Well Telescope is at the far right of the picture.
By courtesy of the National Maritime Museum, London.

Gamma Draconis passed only 4 minutes of arc north of the zenith in Flamsteed's day and since observations would be taken at right angles to the Earth's atmospheric layer, any errors due to atmospheric refraction would be avoided.

An old vertical well about 100 feet deep and 7 feet in diameter in the garden at the observatory, which had no doubt previously served the castle but had now become dry, was provided with a spiral staircase to reach the bottom. At the top of the well, a telescope objective lens 9.7 inches in diameter and of around 87 feet focal length was fixed on top of a vertical open-sided tube at one side of the well. Suspended like a plumb bob vertically below this was the eye-piece of 8 inches focal length, giving a magnification of about 130 times and provided with a graticule for the measurement of very small angles. At the bottom of the well, the observer lay on a couch looking vertically upwards to note the position of the star in the eye-piece. A brave observer would be required for this work as the walls were not bricked up all the way down and there could have been great danger from the walls collapsing or loose stones dropping down the shaft. Also, conditions at the bottom of such a deep well must have been damp, dark and air-less. It is not surprising that no satisfactory results were obtained in this experiment, although the basic idea of measuring small changes in the angle of a star in this way was sound. Flamsteed's well telescope can be considered as the forerunner of zenith telescopes, which some 150 years later measured the parallax of Gamma Draconis as only 0.017 seconds of arc - this being far too small an angle to be measured in Flamsteed's day.

In order to improve his income, John Flamsteed decided to take in pupils who wished to learn about astronomy and mathematics. He would only accept a few students at any given time and a list of their names which he made, in his usual careful fashion, showed that there were altogether around 140 pupils between 1676 and 1709 - that is about four students each year. They were the well-off sons of the nobility and also included Sir Jonas Moore's grandson and others who were the sons of sea-captains or officers of the East India Company. Flamsteed used his pupils to help with his observations of stars during the night and found they were very useful in tasks such as reading the clock at the precise moment a star crossed the meridian or writing down the data he called out to them. The pupils were also an economic benefit and he looked upon their labour as a saving to the government equivalent to the hiring of extra assistants. "This helped to bear the further unavoidable charge of an expensive habitation", Flamsteed wrote. Nevertheless, he was forced to retain one permanent technical assistant, "an ingenious youth," to give him reliable and readily available help.

King Charles regarded his Royal Observatory in part as a training school for navigators and young astronomers and expected the Astronomer Royal to have two boys from the Royal Mathematical School at Christ's Hospital for instruction each month. Flamsteed, rather reluctantly, complied with the king's request but hoped to keep some of the pupils for a longer period so that they would become useful assistants and to some extent "earn their keep." He doubted if he would ever be paid for teaching pupils sent to him by royal authority. As there were no spare beds available at the observatory, he urged Sir Jonas Moore to get Cuthbert Denton to bring over a bed from the Tower so that the pupils could stay at the observatory overnight, rather than having to travel back into town to their own quarters. This would widen their experience and they would be more useful to him. These pupils were "Blue-coat Boys" who studied mathematics and astronomy at Christ Church Hospital and in 1678 Mr. Peter Perkins, the "mathematical master", established a regular arrangement for some of his scholars with John Flamsteed.

The tight financial circumstances under which the Astronomer Royal lived were somewhat relieved by the extra private tutoring he occasionally gave. When writing in 1680 to Seth Ward, Bishop of Salisbury and one of the king's commissioners for the observatory, Flamsteed remarks, "I had a couple of gentlemen to read to: for I am forced to supply the want of my short and ill-paid allowance by my extraordinary labour". Probably Flamsteed enjoyed teaching and he continued to take in pupils for many years, no doubt making contacts with gentlemen of high position and influence in society through teaching their sons. He notes in September 1704, when he was nearing sixty years of age, "I have a couple of young pupils in the house. One of them the son of Lord Ferrers, the other of Sir Matthew Bridges deceased, and his uncle is Surveyor of the Ordnance." Flamsteed had earlier taken these young gentlemen with him to Burstow in Surrey, (where by that time he was rector of the parish), for seven weeks during the summer - continuing their studies during this time. When Flamsteed wrote to Queen Anne in December 1710, he was able to tell her about the useful teaching role he had fulfilled over more than 30 years as Astronomer Royal at Greenwich, during which time he had "educated more than 100 brave youths that have passed into the public service".

The most famous young man to come under Flamsteed's influence however, right at the foundation of the Royal Observatory, was Edmond Halley (1656-1742), who later succeeded Flamsteed as the second Astronomer Royal. Halley's family had moved from Derbyshire to London, where his father was a wealthy merchant and had a soap-boiling business. Halley became a student at Queen's College, Oxford, when he was only 17 years old and even at that age, he possessed a telescope and a sextant and had a good knowledge of the constellations. He visited the site of the Greenwich observatory with Robert Hooke on the 30th of June, 1675, when he was an 18 year- old undergraduate. After this, during his vacations, Halley visited John Flamsteed at the observatory several times and Flamsteed took this very promising young astronomer under his wing. On 15th September, 1676, Sir Jonas Moore, Sir John and Lady Hoskins and Robert Hooke went to the observatory and found Flamsteed and Halley busy setting up the instruments, ready for making the first real observations from that building the next day. Perhaps the enthusiasm and excitement which John Flamsteed showed at this time, when he was newly installed as Astronomer Royal and thrilled by the wide field of investigations open to him, gave Halley the feeling that he too would like to get involved in similar work.

With the assistance of Flamsteed and the Royal Society, Halley gained the backing of King Charles for a project to chart the stars of the southern hemisphere. He therefore left Oxford before taking his degree and set sail in November 1676 on board a British East Indiaman for the remote island of St. Helena, with a grant of

£300 a year from his father and sufficient instruments to set up a small observatory. He returned to Britain in May 1678, having measured the positions of 341 stars, and before the end of that year, he had written his *Catalogus Stellarum Australium*. The speed at which this appeared in print shows the huge difference between the cautious, methodical approach and attention to detail adopted by Flamsteed and the more dynamic style of Halley, who was intent on getting his task speedily concluded in a satisfactory, though perhaps imperfect, fashion. Flamsteed praised the work that his young colleague had performed in the South Atlantic in a letter to Sir Jonas Moore dated July 16th, 1678. But he notes his disappointment that Halley had used information from Tycho's star catalogue as a reference in some places and therefore might have carried over some of Tycho's inaccuracy into the new catalogue. Flamsteed concluded that Halley's work would be "exceeding useful for our sailors" and was a definite enlargement of any previous data but he hoped that his own work would stand alone, avoiding the need to refer to any other man's information and be so accurate as to "need no correction by those that come after us."

In Halley's catalogue of the southern stars he named one constellation *Robur Carolinum* - King Charles's Oak - commemorating the tree in which the king had taken refuge after the battle of Worcester in 1651. This rather shrewd move proved very acceptable to the king and resulted in Halley being granted his M.A. degree at Oxford University by royal mandate. He was also elected a Fellow of the Royal Society at the very early age of 22 years. Flamsteed applauded the work of his young colleague and friend, calling him "the southern Tycho" but not long afterwards he began to see Halley in a different light and there gradually commenced a series of quarrels which was to end in Flamsteed regarding Halley as his bitter enemy.

It appears that teaching appealed to John Flamsteed as offering a more satisfactory career than practical astronomy at this time and his tenure of the post of Astronomer Royal could have been a short one, for, in January 1678, he heard that Dr. Edward Bernard, who occupied the Savilian Chair of Astronomy at Oxford University, was leaving to take up a theological vocation. Both Dr.

Bernard and Mr. Ismael Boulliau (an astronomer who corresponded with Flamsteed) thought that John Flamsteed would make a suitable successor. However, Flamsteed decided not to apply for the position when he was informed by Edward Sherburne of the Office of Ordnance that he could not expect to be appointed to the post seeing he was not an Oxford man. Flamsteed wrote to Dr. Bernard, saying that he would remain content in his post at Greenwich for the time being, despite "the poor air" (possibly a reference to the difficulty he experienced with mist and fog in the Thames estuary which curtailed his observations) and the "distempers" (illnesses) he had suffered there. It seems that there were some obscure movements behind the scenes which influenced Sherburne and possibly others against Flamsteed and prevented his moving into this academic post. Flamsteed, though no doubt a capable teacher and researcher, never occupied a full-time academic position.

CHAPTER VII

The Search for Accuracy

One of the most useful pieces of equipment in Flamsteed's day for the accurate measurement of the positions of the heavenly bodies was the Mural Arc or Wall Quadrant. This would be fixed carefully in a vertical north-south plane and could measure angles from the horizon to the vertex (overhead). John Flamsteed regarded a quadrant as being essential to his work and indeed he had already produced remarkable results with one he had made whilst he lived in Derbyshire, which had a radius of three feet. Robert Hooke had made one of 10 feet radius for the Greenwich Observatory which we have referred to earlier but Flamsteed found this awkward to use and it did not satisfy his requirement for accuracy. It was used only perfunctorily until September 1680.

In June 1678, a quadrant of 40 inches radius fitted with a telescopic sight, designed and made by Hooke for the Royal Society, was procured by Sir Jonas Moore for Flamsteed's use at the Royal Observatory. At first, Flamsteed was not satisfied with Hooke's calibration of this instrument and he proceeded to re-calibrate it to his own required degree of accuracy. It then worked well and was used to find the angle of refraction suffered by rays of starlight when passing through the Earth's atmosphere at different angles above the horizon. When Sir Jonas Moore died, however, Robert Hooke demanded the return of this quadrant to the Royal Society and it was seized from Flamsteed's custody in October 1679. He then decided to make a 50 inch "voluble" (movable) quadrant to his own design. When completed, this gave him great satisfaction, enabling star altitudes to be ascertained to within half a minute of arc and the timing of his clocks to be verified to within three seconds.

Flamsteed knew very well that if he were to publish a catalogue of star positions it had to be superior to the best previously available, which was that based on the observations of 777 stars by Tycho Brahe, expanded later to 1005 by Johannes Kepler and published in 1627 as the *Rudolphine Tables*. Although Flamsteed was a great admirer of Tycho and often referred to him as "the noble Tycho", he knew that Tycho had only made naked-eye observations that could now be considerably improved by the use of telescopic sights. The errors of the *Rudolphine Tables* ruled them out as a means of determining the longitude of a ship at sea. Perhaps the most serious error of Tycho was to make a mistake amounting to 18 minutes of arc in the angle of his meridian. This was discovered by the Frenchman Jean Picard when he went to Hven (the Danish island where Tycho had his famous observatory called "Uraniborg") in 1671 to measure the latitude and longitude accurately so that Tycho's observations could be more closely aligned with those determined elsewhere. Flamsteed's intention was to compile a star catalogue which far exceeded any then available, both in the number of the stars it listed and more importantly, in the greater accuracy with which the positions of the background fixed stars and other celestial bodies had been determined. Flamsteed knew that the king looked to him to provide tables by which navigators could establish their position with a great degree of certainty, so that the lives of sailors who trusted in them and the safety of their cargoes would not be imperilled thereby.

John Flamsteed often felt dissatisfied with the accuracy of his own readings and constantly sought for improvement. He wrote, "I sometimes made above half a minute difference in the height of the same star, taken two several nights but immediately succeeding one another - I grew weary of this work. And though I made some number of observations of meridional heights, I inserted none of them into my catalogues. I knew they ought to be better determined: and I hate to recommend anything to the public of which I am not very certain".

Flamsteed was also seeking to put astronomy on a sound theoretical base, established by accurate observation rather than on the somewhat approximate data of previous astronomers. He wrote down his thoughts as follows, "Coarse observations, made by honest well-meaning men, have more perplexed the astronomer than all their labours and dreams upon them can make him satisfaction for. Their pretty thoughts and conceits in the theories are always excusable and sometimes to be commended. But when rude and ill-managed observations and experiments are brought to confirm them, though they may serve the author's present turn, yet they become a load on the science, and at last turn to his shame and reproach."

A question of accuracy was indirectly to lead to the first disagreement between John Flamsteed and his young friend and colleague, Edmond Halley. It concerned the observations which the experienced Polish astronomer, Johannes Hevelius, was producing for his star catalogues, which were eventually published posthumously by his wife in 1687 as *Catalogus Stellarum Fixarum* together with a further publication of data on 1564 stars and accompanying star maps in 1690. Hevelius preferred to measure star positions by naked-eye sightings, without a telescope. Flamsteed knew that by using a quadrant or sextant fitted with a telescopic sight, the resultant magnification could produce significant gains in accuracy. He had rejected naked-eye quadrant observations in a letter which was published in the *Philosophical Transactions* of the Royal Society in December 1672 – a publication which not only circulated in Britain but was also widely read on the continent. Robert Hooke expressed the same opinion very strongly and their criticism tended to disparage the whole of Hevelius' life's work. Because his reputation and the value of his entire published work was challenged, Hevelius responded sharply to Flamsteed's criticism. He claimed a precision of 30 seconds of arc in repeated measurements made at the same sitting or 60 seconds in measurements made at different times for the position of a particular star. When Flamsteed had obtained a similar degree of precision we have seen that he "grew weary of this work" and excluded such readings from his catalogue, because he strove for better accuracy.

The Royal Society decided to send Edmond Halley to investigate Hevelius' claims and to perform telescopic measurements alongside him in a comparison of techniques. Halley set out for Danzig (modern-day Gdansk) where Hevelius had his observatory in 1679 and after some time as a summer guest in Hevelius' house Halley reported back. He said that he had been surprised by the high level of agreement between his own measurements and those of the elderly astronomer and therefore he gave his support to Hevelius' claim to accuracy. Flamsteed believed Halley had not been entirely honest in his report and had been far too generous in his acceptance of the outmoded technique Hevelius used, or perhaps he thought Halley had been rather careless in his own observations. Halley later admitted that he had reported with something of a bias in Hevelius' favour so as not to bring about the loss of reputation, or even the death, of "an old and peevish gentleman" and "I would not hasten his departure by exposing him and his observations as I could do, and truly as I think he deserves I should." The matter was complicated further when, soon after Halley's visit, Hevelius' observatory (which was built on top of his house) caught fire, destroying most of his instruments, books and notes. This was a terrible blow for the 68 year old astronomer, who had yet to publish his main results. Nevertheless, he constructed another observatory, which was in use by 1681. Flamsteed was very sympathetic towards Hevelius because of the calamity that had befallen him as he neared the end of his career and he sent him telescope objectives of 8, 16 and 24 feet focal lengths as well as a micrometer so that he could replace some of the instruments lost in the fire. Flamsteed left the micrometer uncalibrated so that Hevelius would investigate its mode of operation and perform the calibration to his own liking.

Flamsteed desired to see the utmost accuracy in published data, obtained by using the most up-to-date instruments available, so that the scientist or navigator could use such data with implicit reliability. He was aware that errors of observation would arise with any measuring instrument and much of his time was taken up by calibrating his own instruments on a regular basis and correcting their readings for every possible error. Now, although he doubted that Hevelius' results were sufficiently accurate to meet his own strict criteria, he was prepared to be sympathetic to the plight of this veteran astronomer. He declined to challenge the old man further, declaring, "He is very old, has obliged the World much by his labours, has taken a vast deal of paines and been at great cost to publish them, he has suffered much of late and it would look like a piece of inhumanity to vex him with an examination of his works under these circumstances."

One particular experiment Flamsteed regularly carried out was designed to test the accuracy of his readings of the east-west positions of stars. He took seven stars which were at almost the same altitude of 15 degrees above the horizon (in order to eliminate refraction errors due to the Earth's atmosphere) and measured the east-west angles between them. The seven angles should add together to make exactly 360 degrees. In one test, in the year 1679, for which the figures still exist, the sum came to 359 degrees 59 minutes 22 seconds - an error of only 38 seconds in seven intermutual distances. This was the kind of accuracy which Flamsteed required and he must have been pleased with such a satisfactory result.

Because of the disappointing results obtained with the 10 foot quadrant made by Robert Hooke when the observatory had been opened, Flamsteed decided to construct another to his own design. With the assistance of a local workman and at a cost of a little under £100, he made a Mural Arc of 6 feet 9 inches radius which could cover 140 degrees of the sky and observe any star in the northern hemisphere. This was ready in August 1681. Unfortunately, this also was not a very good device because of its rather slight construction and also its tendency to warp. After calibrating it carefully, Flamsteed used it from 1683 to 1686, though he was never very confident in the readings he took with it. Parts of this instrument were subsequently reused in constructing a greatly improved Mural Arc in 1689 (see Appendix 1 D) which became Flamsteed's favourite instrument for accurate observation over the next thirty years.

A great blow to John Flamsteed occurred with the sudden death of his friend and supporter Sir Jonas Moore at Godalming in

Surrey on 27th August, 1679, when Sir Jonas was returning from a visit to Portsmouth. The establishment of the Royal Observatory and the appointment of John Flamsteed as Astronomer Royal owed a great deal to the patronage of Sir Jonas in his position as Surveyor-General of Ordnance and in other ways, too, he had used his influence with the king to advance scientific activities in Britain. Partly in recognition of the help he had received from Sir Jonas Moore, Flamsteed assisted with the editing of his final textbook on mathematics, entitled *New Systeme of the Mathematicks*, which was published posthumously in 1681. Flamsteed contributed a rather complex section to this publication entitled *Doctrine of the Sphere Grounded on the Motion of the Earth*, basing this firmly upon Copernican principles.

This sad loss of his patron and friend dashed Flamsteed's hopes of obtaining further instruments or the money to pay for them, from the government through the Surveyor-General of Ordnance. Indeed, he had a hard struggle to prevent Sir Jonas Moore's son taking away equipment from the observatory on the grounds that his father had only loaned the instruments to the Astronomer Royal but this removal was prevented by the action of the Board of Ordnance. Flamsteed was also worried about the continuance of his salary, which had been paid through the Ordnance Office and he took the step of writing to Dr. Seth Ward, giving an account of the work he had done and his achievements both in the field of astronomy and in navigation. Seth Ward had been Professor of Astronomy at Oxford University from 1649 to 1661 and was a great friend of Sir Christopher Wren. In both these men Flamsteed would have found capable judges of his work and people who were keen to see the Royal Observatory, of which they were Commissioners, make its mark on contemporary astronomy.

A further blow to Flamsteed came with the death of King Charles II in February 1685. Although the king had not been very closely concerned with the work that his royal astronomer had been doing at Greenwich, he had been well disposed towards the young John Flamsteed at the time the observatory had been built and Flamsteed would no doubt have been well received by the king if he had needed to approach him or seek his support. Flamsteed had now lost his royal sponsor and perhaps wondered if his position would be abolished. In the event, he need not have worried as his small salary continued to be paid and the position of Astronomer Royal has remained until the present day.

John Flamsteed's father, Stephen, also died, on 8th March, 1688 and this was perhaps the hardest blow of all. He had received the best possible upbringing by his father, following the early death of his mother when he was only three years old and the best medical attention which could be found. No doubt Stephen Flamsteed had hoped that his only son would follow him into the family business but he never stood in the way when John decided to go to London to pursue his interest in astronomy. With his father now dead, Flamsteed's roots in Derbyshire were severed. He had lost the degree of security which having a reasonably well-off father in the family business at Derby had provided and he would not be able to return there if things turned out badly for him in London. On the other hand, he had inherited a sum of money from his father's estate which was very useful to someone in his tight financial position. He determined to use some of his inheritance on the construction of the instrument he had wanted from the time he first moved in to the observatory - a really good Mural Arc which would perform better than any of his previous Arcs or Quadrants.

He was fortunate to have at this time an exceedingly capable assistant, Mr. Abraham Sharp, who had recently joined him at the observatory - though he had previously assisted him there for a six-month period in 1684. Abraham Sharp was an excellent geometer and mathematician and also "a most expert and curious mechanic," who today would be called a skilled instrument maker. In August 1688, Abraham Sharp began to construct, under John Flamsteed's watchful eye, a 7-foot radius Mural Arc which was a great improvement on anything they had used before (see Appendix 1, D). The careful design and workmanship which went into this instrument meant that it was not completed until 14 months later and was estimated to have cost Flamsteed more than £120. This Arc covered an angle of about 140 degrees from the southern horizon and thus was capable of sighting and measuring the position of any object in the sky visible from Greenwich. It was "divided" or graduated by Abraham Sharp - one of the most skilled persons in Britain at this task. (The scale from another brass quadrant also graduated by Sharp can be seen at the Greenwich observatory today.) At its completion, the 7-foot Mural Arc was carefully fixed on the meridional west wall of the Quadrant House and it was ready for its first real work in September 1689. The radial arm carrying the moveable 7-foot long telescope could be adjusted through very small angles by the revolution of a tangential screw-wheel which was radially divided into 100 parts. Flamsteed knew that the screw thread mechanism was not perfect and he made a table for converting the graduations of the screw into minutes and seconds of arc. The vertical alignment of the instrument was accurately carried out using a plumb-line and checked periodically to ensure the circumferential scale of degrees remained true. The moving arm was counter-balanced for ease of use and because only sightings in the north-south meridian were to be taken, the telescope pointed through an aperture 18 inches wide running north-south in the roof of the observation house. This aperture was revealed by sliding back only part of the roof and not only did this make conditions much more comfortable for the observers but the exclusion of stray ambient light was found to allow stars down to magnitude seven to be seen with the naked eye. It was soon realised that this was a truly excellent instrument, which was as reliable as the sextant which Flamsteed used. Flamsteed rejoiced at the acquisition of this new instrument and wrote, "One good instrument is of as much worth as a hundred indifferent ones". At last, he had obtained the accurate and trustworthy piece of equipment that he had desired since the observatory opened in 1676.

In addition to the two Great Clocks in the Octagon Room, which were the standard reference clocks kept accurate by stellar sightings, Flamsteed had other pendulum clocks to use in his work. In the Sextant and Quadrant House he had a secondary standard clock to use in his recordings of transit times, which again was made for him by Thomas Tompion. This had a pendulum which beat at one second intervals and probably the audible ticking of this clock every second would help the observer to take the altitude reading of a celestial object at exactly the right moment. The first clock in the "Arc House", which probably ran for one week without winding, was replaced in 1690 by another similar clock; again this was Flamsteed's own property.

Another interesting clock, which can still be seen in the Meridian Room at Greenwich where Flamsteed would have used it, was a Sidereal or "Degree Clock" made by Tompion in 1691 (see Appendix 1, I and figure 27). The pendulum of this clock beat three times in two seconds and the dial enabled one to read time relative to the fixed stars, or to Earth's rotation, as an angle to the north-south meridian.

To the left of the door leading into the Octagon Room as one entered (the Great Clocks are to the right) was another clock with a similar dial to the Great Clocks. This clock could have been made under the supervision of Richard Towneley and it had a 6-foot pendulum. The dial was decorated by Tompion as an exact match for the other two and was probably installed along with them in 1676.

Thus the lack of a good pendulum clock, which Flamsteed had so much regretted when he lived at home in Derbyshire, was now remedied. The Royal Observatory at Greenwich was set on its course for accurately timed positional determinations of the heavenly bodies which would eventually make possible the kind of reliable navigation at sea which Flamsteed had envisaged and which eventually established Greenwich Mean Time as an international standard of reference.

CHAPTER VIII

Lectures at Gresham College

Sir Thomas Gresham (1519-1579), son of a former Lord Mayor of London, was a wealthy merchant and financier who advised Queen Elizabeth the First on economic matters and founded the Royal Exchange in London - a finance house to rival the most famous in Europe. Following the death of his only son, Sir Thomas Gresham became a great philanthropist, causing almshouses to be built and many other charitable institutions to be established. He was also interested in education for the general public and on his death he bequeathed money for the institution of a college in London in which lectures were to be given in Divinity, Physic (Medicine), Astronomy, Geometry, Law, Rhetoric and Music.

By the middle of the 17th Century, Gresham College had become a famous centre of learning, particularly in mathematics and astronomy and members of the Royal Society gathered there for their weekly meetings. Robert Hooke was Gresham Professor of Geometry but his interests ranged very widely over many branches of science and there is no doubt that his lectures strayed well outside the bounds of geometry. Sir Christopher Wren, one of the brightest men of his time, had been appointed Professor of Astronomy at Gresham College in 1657 but had afterwards moved on to Oxford. In 1680, the Professor of Astronomy at Gresham was Walter Pope, who suffered a severe illness which nearly caused him to lose his sight. Because of this illness, Pope invited John

Flamsteed to take over his lectures at Gresham College and records show that Flamsteed gave at least 39 discourses on astronomy between April 1681 and November 1684.

It will be remembered that Sir Jonas Moore, Flamsteed's patron, had died in 1679 and there followed a period when Flamsteed was rather concerned about his future security as Astronomer Royal and the threat to his already poor financial position. To be asked to give lectures at Gresham College would have been a welcome way for Flamsteed to earn a little more at this time of uncertainty and as he was already teaching young pupils at the observatory, it was an activity not entirely new to him and was likely to present little difficulty. It is possible that Flamsteed gave up lecturing at Gresham College at the end of 1684 because during that year he was granted the living of the Parish of Burstow in Surrey and as a Church of England clergyman he then had an established source of income. He remained in residence at the Royal Observatory, of course, for the rest of his life and only visited Burstow occasionally - mainly during the summer months and at Christmas. When his star atlas, *Atlas Coelestis* was published in 1729, Flamsteed was referred to as "Regius Professor of Astronomy at Greenwich" and the justification for this title could have been this period when he provided the astronomy lectures at Gresham College.

At this time, the brilliantly innovative work of Sir Isaac Newton on gravitation and optics still awaited publication – these great ideas remaining in virtual isolation at Cambridge amongst a few of Newton's colleagues and students who probably understood little about them. Newton's *Philosophiae Naturalis Principia Mathematica* was only printed in 1687 and his *Optics* in 1704. So John Flamsteed did not have the benefit of a knowledge of Newton's revolutionary work when he gave his series of lectures at Gresham College, although he was in regular correspondence with Newton on matters relating to astronomy and supplied him with data on the positions of the heavenly bodies which he needed for his theoretical work.

The Gresham Lectures of John Flamsteed show that he was familiar with the ideas and equipment used by the ancient Greek and Arabian astronomers, with their measurements and the philosophies which framed their thoughts on the universe. He continually referred to these early men, who sometimes had arrived at conclusions which were well ahead of their times. On the other hand he was not afraid to criticise some of the ideas of these long-dead philosophers, nor to show the fallacies of more recent astronomers, when he had the evidence to prove his point. He was grateful for the records of the ancient astronomers, which indicated that the general shape and arrangement of the constellations had not changed in 2000 years and the obliquity of the ecliptic was unchanged from the time of the Greeks. Flamsteed taught that the stars appear fixed because of their vast distances from the Earth, that their respective positions as seen from the Earth had not changed throughout historical times, and that the Earth continued to revolve with its axis having the same orientation in space. "The fixed stars are the basis of astronomy," declared Flamsteed and observations of the stars occupied most of his time. He rejected the idea of the ancients of concentric revolving orbs bearing the planets, since he had observed comets travelling from vast distances in space to approach the Earth and yet they did not shatter these "celestial spheres", neither were they impeded by them in their paths. He agreed with Galileo, Kepler and Descartes that the stars generate their own light, independently of the Sun, whereas the planets and the Moon only reflect the Sun's light. Telescopes had shown that the planets had spherical shapes and that Mercury and Venus exhibited phases like the Moon, demonstrating that they receive their light from the Sun and have orbits inside the Earth's orbit - consistent with the Copernican view of the solar system. Mars was seen to be always more than half illuminated by the Sun – showing its orbit to be outside that of the Earth, whilst Jupiter and Saturn appear always to be almost fully illuminated due to their great distances from Earth and Sun. The shadows cast by the satellites of Jupiter on its disc and the eclipses of these satellites when they pass into Jupiter's shadow, show that Jupiter relies on the Sun for its light. Similarly, Flamsteed reasoned, the ring around Saturn casts a shadow on its disc and therefore, light from the Sun must also be responsible for that planet's illumination.

On a practical note, Flamsteed described in his lectures the manufacture and use of Parallactic Rulers (illustrated in the diagram below), which had been used for astronomical measurements since the time of Ptolemy at least. He criticised this piece of equipment, by which the ancients had derived their figures of star positions: and examined its experimental accuracy. Errors were inevitable for several reasons;

a) the observers were not sure of the true meridian at which to measure their angles,

b) they had no accurate clocks with which to time their readings,

c) the construction, whether of wood or metal, would suffer from manufacturing errors, such as loose joints and particularly in the hot climate of eastern lands, would be subject to warping or expansion and contraction of the rulers,

d) they knew nothing of angular errors caused by atmospheric refraction, though Flamsteed reckoned he could correct these if he knew the latitude of their observatories.

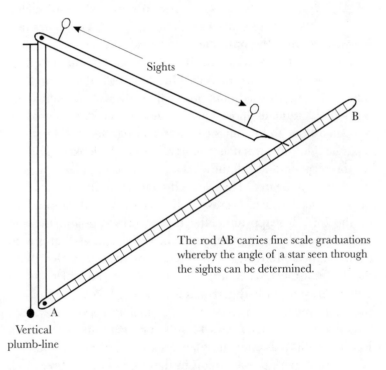

Sights

B

The rod AB carries fine scale graduations whereby the angle of a star seen through the sights can be determined.

A

Vertical
plumb-line

Figure 8.
Diagram of "Parallactic Rulers" as used by the ancient astronomers.

Flamsteed brought any work on which he had recently been engaged into his Gresham lectures. For instance, he estimated the Earth's orbital diameter to be about 163 million miles (modern value around 186 million miles) and the diameter of the Sun to be about 1/220th of that distance, thus giving the Sun a diameter of 741,000 miles (compared to the modern estimate of 865,000 miles). These dimensions were revealed in his lectures to an audience which had been accustomed to believe that distances in the solar system were an order of magnitude smaller than we know them to be today. It is remarkable that with fairly simple apparatus he could arrive at such reasonably close estimates of these huge dimensions.

The relative brightness of the Sun and stars led Flamsteed to conclude that, as they were in his opinion basically of the same nature, they were at considerably different distances - and the brightest stars must be those nearest to Earth. He also related how he had observed sunspots and had calculated the Sun's rate of rotation from the movement of these spots across the disc, supposing that they resulted from a kind of volcanic eruption originating deep inside the Sun. One sunspot first seen on 27th July, 1679, when it was about one-sixth of the distance across the Sun's disc, gradually moved across the disc and disappeared on 5th August due to the Sun's rotation. During this time, he saw it separate into three less dense spots and when he looked carefully for the reappearance of these spots, fourteen days later, he saw they had disappeared. He observed a longer-lasting sunspot first on 16th October, which crossed the Sun's disc and disappeared on the 23rd. It reappeared after the semi-revolution of the Sun on 9th November and continued to be visible until it disappeared again on the 20th. It was seen to return on the 6th of December but was now much paler and it finally disappeared on December 15th. This sunspot had persisted for about 60 days and from its motion Flamsteed estimated the Sun's rotational period to be 25.25 days sidereal time or 27 days 4 hours apparent time as seen from Earth, with its axis tilted at an angle of 7 degrees. This estimate of the Sun's period of rotation in the sunspot zone agrees well with the modern value of 27 days 7 hours as seen from Earth.

Because the Sun rotated, Flamsteed assumed that the stars

would do so also and that their brightness might vary, due to spots on their surfaces, at a rate which would depend on their rotational speed. He conjectured that this might explain variable stars and also the rare sudden appearance of new stars. Although the fixed stars had seemed to be static and without change for the past two thousand years, Flamsteed realised that there were dynamic processes taking place inside the Sun and stars which could occasionally produce the startling variability in brightness which Tycho, Kepler and he himself had observed. In the course of his lectures, he described the new star which, according to Tycho, had appeared on November 11th, 1572, in Cassiopeia and was at first brighter than Sirius or Jupiter and almost as bright as Venus, being visible in daylight to some people. By December, the star had diminished, becoming equal to Jupiter and by the following December was only a 5th magnitude star. It had been very white at first, but afterwards turned to yellow and then became more reddish like, Mars or Aldebaran. Another new star had appeared in October 1604, being seen by Kepler at about the brightness of Venus or Jupiter but declining to the 3rd magnitude by April 1605 and going through the same colour changes – from white to yellow and then a dull red. These would be termed novae or supernovae nowadays and they demonstrated that the universe was not fixed and changeless, as most people then believed but that some limited parts were subject to sudden and dramatic change. Flamsteed, himself, had probably seen the new but less bright 3rd magnitude star that had appeared in Cygnus in 1600 and had continued to diminish only very gradually until it became barely visible to the naked eye as a 6th magnitude star in 1680. Flamsteed had difficulty, of course, in explaining these phenomena in his Gresham lectures but he believed they might in some way be similar to sunspot variations. A further 300 years were to pass before a reasonably satisfactory explanation could be given, based on the knowledge of nuclear physics gained in the 20th Century.

The subject of optics was dealt with in several lectures and here Flamsteed had the benefit of having seen the papers left by William Gascoigne, the north-country astronomer from Middleton near Leeds, who fell at the battle of Marston Moor during the Civil War. Flamsteed learnt much of his optics from Gascoigne's theories and incorporated this work into his Gresham Lectures. Starting with the refraction of light in a plane-sided block of refractive index 1.5, Flamsteed went on to discuss the optical properties of a plano-convex and a bi-convex lens and how lenses with a spherical surface could never produce a perfectly focused image. The application of convex lenses in Keplerian telescopes (see Appendix F) was dealt with and Flamsteed taught that the convex side of a plano-convex lens should always be towards the stars when used as the object glass of such a telescope in order to obtain the best image. He advocated the use of thin lenses and long focal lengths to overcome optical aberrations and to obtain the best resolution in the image. These lectures also dealt with refraction by concave lenses and their use as the eye-pieces of Galilean telescopes (see Appendix E) and he compared the two types of refractor. The Newtonian design of reflector telescope was also described (see Appendix H) and it was shown how this avoided the chromatic aberration present with lenses, but Newtonian telescopes were difficult to construct and had other disadvantages. The speculum metal (an alloy of tin and copper), of which the mirror was made, was not easily ground and polished to the curvature required and reflects only about 60% of the light falling on it when newly finished. It afterwards tarnishes rather rapidly. It was also difficult to attach micrometers in a reflector or to fit the telescope to a quadrant. Reflector telescopes, therefore, were rarely used before about 1740, when James Short, in Edinburgh, succeeded in routinely grinding concave mirrors and producing such telescopes commercially.

Flamsteed covered many practical aspects of astronomy in his lectures. He described the use of cross-wires or silkworm threads placed at the focus of the telescope as an aid in determining the positions of stars more accurately and also the micrometer (first used by Gascoigne around 1638) for measuring the diameters of planets or the very small angles between adjacent stars or planets in the field of view. The accurate setting up of a quadrant for the measurement of the altitude of stars above the horizon was a task in which Flamsteed excelled and this was also dealt with in his lectures at Gresham College.

Further lecture topics concerned work in which Flamsteed was currently engaged or which he had recently completed and these would spring readily to mind when he was invited to give his lectures. He was interested in finding the dimensions of the solar system and its geometry and his discourses went into the determination of the solar parallax (which gave an estimate of the distance from the Earth to the Sun), the obliquity of the ecliptic (the tilt of the Earth's axis relative to the plane of its orbit around the Sun), the precession of the equinoxes (due to the slow change in the direction of Earth's axis), first noticed by the Greek astronomer, Hipparchus around 120 B.C., which is caused by the gravitational attraction of the Sun and Moon on the equatorial bulge of the Earth but which was not explained until Newton published his *Principia*, and finding the distance from Earth to the Moon. Flamsteed's observations of comets, which included two very bright ones that had caused widespread public interest and on the refraction of light in the atmosphere (which necessitates a correction in the observed altitude of a star to obtain the true position), were also part of his Gresham lectures. These subjects will be more fully discussed in a later chapter.

John Flamsteed's lectures at Gresham College took place over only four years and there seems to be evidence that some lectures were not well attended. The college would only be available to persons living nearby and as it was not empowered to grant degrees it had not the same attraction as the Universities at Oxford or Cambridge. The professors at Gresham College however, included some very famous men, such as Sir Christopher Wren and Robert Hooke, not to mention John Flamsteed and it was the base for the weekly meetings of the Royal Society from which ideas disseminated to other universities. Because of the practical approach to learning which was established at Gresham College it had a good influence on the traditional universities, which in some ways were rather inclined to be inward-looking centres of book-learning.

Flamsteed himself was not impressed by the teaching which went on at Oxford or Cambridge. He considered that "mathematics languishes in both Universities in spite of the munificence of generous benefactors and the noble designs of persons of public spirit." Both universities had excellent mathematicians, Isaac Newton in Cambridge and John Wallis in Oxford, with whom Flamsteed corresponded but it is likely that these brilliant mathematicians gave very few lectures themselves and made little difference to the routine teaching in their colleges. One of Flamsteed's correspondents, Stephen Gray, who was an impecunious dyer from Canterbury and a very keen but self-taught amateur astronomer, went to study at Cambridge in 1708, but he left after only a few months. He told Flamsteed that he already knew as much as they were teaching him at the university and that he should have taken Flamsteed's earlier advice and not gone there in the first place as it had been a complete waste of his time.

It was also common for casual students to attend the universities but to leave before taking their degree. Records show that at about this time only some 40% of undergraduates at Oxford stayed on to take their B.A. degree and then only 24% went on to the M.A. We have seen how the young Edmond Halley had left Oxford before taking his degree in order to make observations of the southern stars and was only granted the M.A. degree, by royal command, on his return from St. Helena.

Another contribution in the field of education was made by John Flamsteed when he helped set up the syllabuses in navigation and astronomy for the Royal Mathematical School, a school for boys, founded in 1673 within Christ's Hospital – which itself was a medieval institution and by the 17th Century had become the chief school in the City of London. These subjects were important in a seafaring port such as London and in great demand. Flamsteed designed courses which were practical in content and developed a good understanding of the subject, including the use of telescopes fitted with micrometers, quadrants, pendulums, maps, charts and magnetic compasses. The blue-coat boys from Christ's Hospital were regularly sent to Flamsteed at the Greenwich observatory for tuition and some of his students became useful assistants in his work. Flamsteed was probably a strict disciplinarian who expected good results from his pupils, following the pattern of his own Puritan schoolmasters at Derby and he was able to produce capable and reliable astronomers and navigators who remained loyal to him in their later years. In his rules for the school, he made provision for the encouragement of pupils by laying down that those boys who improved most during the term (as shown by the examination marks given by an external examiner) should receive rewards or prizes for their good work. Flamsteed himself was asked to give theoretical and practical assistance with that part of the course dealing with astronomy and was also an occasional examiner. It is apparent, therefore, that Flamsteed contributed widely to specialist education in the field of astronomy from his position as a practising astronomer of international repute.

CHAPTER IX

Giving Dimensions to the Heavens

As the Copernican theory of the Solar System gained gradual acceptance during the first half of the 17th Century, there remained the questions: "What is the radius of Earth's orbit around the Sun?" and " Just how far away is the Moon from Earth?" Flamsteed knew that the stars, which had not changed their relative positions as seen from Earth over a period of 2000 years and were, therefore, known as the fixed stars, appeared not to move because they were at immense distances from observers on Earth. But the distances of the Moon and the Sun would not be as great and so, could he measure these distances and thereby put a scale to the heavens?

The method Flamsteed used to find the distance of the Sun from Earth was to measure the change in angle of the Sun with respect to the fixed stars from the morning to the evening, when the rotation of the Earth would have changed the observer's position in space by a distance equal to Earth's diameter (see figure 9). This is known as the Sun's diurnal parallax and is a very small angle indeed. Because the Sun and stars cannot be observed at the same time, Flamsteed measured the angle between the Sun and Mars and then between Mars and two fixed stars which appeared close to it. He obtained the result that the solar parallax was less than 10 seconds of arc, as shown in the diagram, and this meant that the Sun was much further away than anyone before had supposed. At first, Flamsteed was cautious about this result, which he had first arrived at in 1672 when he still lived in Derbyshire and he repeated it at least three times afterwards from the observatory at Greenwich between 1676 and 1681. In a letter to his friend, John Collins, at the Royal Society in February 1673, he writes, "I have certainly learnt from my observations that the Sun's parallax is not above 10 seconds, yea probably but 7 seconds, and his distance *a terra* 26,000 semi-diameters of the Earth, which is a distance to which none ever durst remove him yet and thrice as far off as I supposed him formerly in my solar tables". In July 1673, he communicated this result to Cassini, the Director of the Paris Observatory, but being just a little more cautious, he quotes the Sun's parallax as "at most 10 seconds" and the Earth-Sun distance as 21,000 terrestrial radii. It is interesting to note that Edmond Halley assisted Flamsteed at one of these solar parallax measurements on January 14th, 1679, when the two men were still friends.

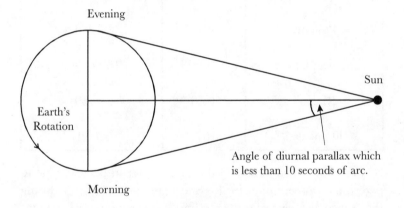

Figure 9.
Diagram illustrating the measurement of solar parallax, which enabled the Sun's distance to be found.

If we take Flamsteed's value of 10 seconds of arc and the value of Earth's radius, which the Frenchman Jean Picard had reported in his 1671 publication *Mesure de la Terre* as 3953 miles, of which Flamsteed would have been aware, calculation gives the Sun's distance from Earth as about 82 million miles. A modern value for the average distance is about 93 million miles and the solar parallax is more accurately measured as 8.8 seconds. Although Flamsteed's results were somewhat adrift from the correct values, they startled the scientific men of his period because, in Flamsteed's words, "The Sun is and ever was above ten times more remote than commonly esteemed". The gradually increasing values which ingenious astronomers, at different times, had given for the Sun's distance in terms of the radius of the Earth is shown in the table below.

INVESTIGATOR	DATE APPROX	SUN'S DISTANCE IN TERMS OF EARTH'S RADIUS
Pythagorus	550 BC	180 - 360
Hipparchus	140 BC	1140
Ptolemy	140 AD	1210
Kepler	1620	1800 -3470
Riccioli	1651	1460
Flamsteed	1672	20624

John Flamsteed also used the micrometer in his telescope to determine the variation in the Sun's apparent diameter during the course of a year and thus to find the variation in its distance from Earth due to the eccentricity of the Earth's elliptical orbit. This had previously been done by Giovanni Riccioli, who timed the transit of the Sun's image across a thread in the field of his telescope at different times of the year, but Flamsteed was able to measure the image of the Sun's disc directly using his micrometer. The Sun actually comes closest to Earth each year on January 3rd (91.4 million miles) and is furthest away on July 4th (94.5 million miles), which is rather convenient for those who live in the northern hemisphere!

From the earliest times, it had been obvious that the Moon has an apparent diameter approximately equal to that of the Sun and in a solar eclipse almost exactly blocks out the Sun's disc - thus it must be closer to Earth than the Sun and actually have a smaller diameter. But what is its distance from the Earth? By some rather clever reasoning and with an accurate knowledge of the positions of the fixed stars which the Moon intercepts in its path across the heavens, it was possible, in Flamsteed's time, to calculate the distance of the Moon from Earth quite accurately. A simplified explanation of this reasoning can be given with reference to the diagram below.

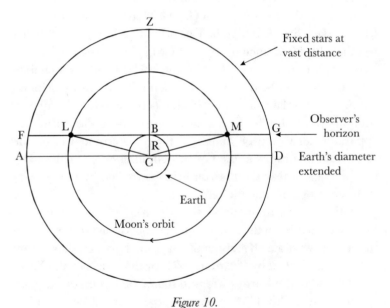

Figure 10.
Diagram illustrating Flamsteed's measurement of the Moon's horizontal parallax, whereby he obtained the distance from the Earth to the Moon.

In this diagram (which is not to scale) the Earth is centred at C and is of radius R. The Moon travels in a roughly circular path around the Earth and the fixed stars at vast distances from Earth are represented by the outer circle. The positions of the stars on this outer circle were accurately measured by Flamsteed as one of his main tasks and they can be considered as providing angle graduations around the circle of stars. Consider an observer at B on Earth's circumference, whose horizon will be the line FG and his zenith Z, whilst Earth's diameter extended will be the line ACD. The Moon completes an orbit in around 28 days or moves from A to D in the star background in about 14 days.

The observer at B, however, sees the Moon appear on his horizon when it is in its orbit at L, coinciding with the fixed star at F and sees it disappear on the opposite horizon when it is at M, coinciding with the fixed star at G. The Moon's passage from L to M will take a little less than half its orbital period (i.e. somewhat less than 14 days), since the angle LCM is less than 180 degrees. Accurate timing and reference to the background stars enables the angle BLC to be determined, which is known as the Moon's "horizontal parallax". Its value, of about one degree, had probably been arrived at by the Greek astronomers using their primitive apparatus but would be more accurately determined using the clocks and quadrants at the Greenwich observatory, with angles of observation near the horizon being corrected by Flamsteed's knowledge of atmospheric refraction.

With his measurement of the Moon's horizontal parallax, Flamsteed arrived at the conclusion that the Moon's distance from the centre of the Earth is about 60 times the Earth's radius. Using the value published by Picard in 1671 for the radius of the Earth as 3953 miles, the Earth - Moon distance thus comes to around 237 thousand miles. This is very close to the value accepted today for the Moon's mean distance of 239 thousand miles, with the eccentricity of the orbit producing variations from 226 to 252 thousand miles.

As we have previously mentioned, by using the micrometer fitted to his telescope Flamsteed was able to measure the seasonal variation in the apparent size of both the Sun and the Moon's discs and thus to gain some idea of the eccentricity of the orbits of the Earth and the Moon. Also, because he had determined the distance from Earth of these two major heavenly bodies, with the knowledge of their angular diameters he was able to calculate their true diameters reasonably accurately. The diameter of the Moon could also be arrived at very approximately by observing the shadow that the Earth casts on the Moon's disc during a lunar eclipse, if the diameter of the Earth were known. Probably Flamsteed used this as an additional check on his calculations but his measurement of the Moon's horizontal parallax and its angular diameter would give him a far more accurate value than had been available to the earlier astronomers.

To arrive at a "theory of the Moon" which would enable him to predict the position of the Moon in relation to the background stars was one of Flamsteed's principal objectives, as he knew this would make possible more accurate navigation on the high seas - for which purpose the Royal Observatory had been founded. He knew the mean radius and the eccentricity of the Moon's orbit but this was still insufficient to solve the problem. The great Tycho had attempted "to resolve the Moon's wanderings, which are tangled in bewildering complexity", and he commented, "Its intricate movement has tormented us for many years with its incredible labour". Flamsteed tried to solve the Moon's wanderings by arriving at empirical equations which could be used to predict its position in the sky but found it was extremely difficult to determine a lunar position for some future time which would agree with the observation. He gave Sir Isaac Newton some 150 accurate positions of the Moon which he had observed in 1694 and 1695 but even with Newton's intimate knowledge of gravitational theory it was impossible for him to predict future positions to better than about 10 minutes of arc (about one third of the Moon's disc) and this was still not good enough for accurate navigational purposes. It was not until 1755, following nearly 20 years of lunar observation by Halley at Greenwich and intense efforts by many European mathematicians, that the astronomer Tobias Mayer of Gottingen produced satisfactory tables of the Sun and Moon. These were tested by the British Admiralty, in 1761, on a sea voyage to St. Helena and were found to give the longitude to better than one degree. Encouraged by this, Nevil Maskelyne, the fifth Astronomer

Royal, published the *British Mariner's Guide* in 1763 and the *Nautical Almanac* from 1767, which enabled sea captains to establish their longitude with satisfactory accuracy for safe navigation. This second publication has become an annual production of course, continued until the present day.

To measure the distance from Earth to the stars was obviously a very difficult project but Flamsteed thought that by using the movement of the Earth around its orbit to obtain two observations separated by a 6-monthly interval when Earth would be at opposite ends of an orbital diameter, i.e. some 163 million miles apart according to his knowledge of the Earth-Sun distance, he could use this as a long baseline from which to measure the angular movement of a star or its "annual parallax". By measurements of the position of the Pole Star, taken in March and in the following September, Flamsteed arrived at a figure for this angular change as "not more than 50 seconds of arc" or, more precisely, 48 seconds. Such a figure would indicate an Earth-star distance of over 700 billion miles but this falls far short of the distance to even the nearest star, Alpha Centauri, which is 4.3 light-years from Earth. The angle which Flamsteed measured was probably that due to the relative speeds of the Earth through space and the speed of light, which is known as the "aberration of light" (see figures 11a and 11b). This effect was unknown in Flamsteed's day, although (following a visit which the Danish astronomer Olaus Romer had made to Greenwich in 1679) he knew about the finite velocity of light and the effect this had on the observed times of eclipse of Jupiter's satellites as the planet moved closer to, or further from, the Earth. After this visit and Romer's explanation, Flamsteed designed and constructed a "Jovilabe" which was able to demonstrate the positions of Jupiter's four known satellites. The aberration of light was observed and explained by James Bradley (the 3rd Astronomer Royal at Greenwich) around 1727. Its effect would be to produce an apparent change in angle of a star over a 6-monthly interval of about 41 seconds of arc, which is close to the value which Flamsteed observed and which was published as part of John Wallis's *Opera Mathematica* in Oxford in 1699.

The Aberration of Light

Figure 11a.

Diagram illustrating how the umbrella of a walking man must be tilted in the direction of travel if it is to provide cover over all of his body. In a similar manner a telescope must be tilted slightly in the direction of Earth's motion through space in order that light photons will emerge from the eye-piece.

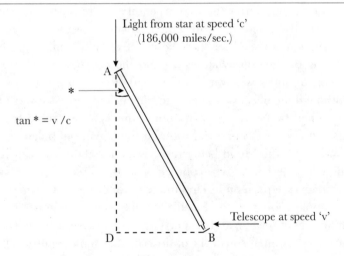

Light from star at speed 'c'
(186,000 miles/sec.)

tan * = v /c

Telescope at speed 'v'

Figure 11b.

Diagram illustrating how the aberration of light necessitates the tilting of a telescope through an angle * to compensate for the lateral speed of the telescope 'v' with respect to the vertically falling light photons of speed 'c'.

Several ancient astronomers, beginning with Eratosthenes in about 240 BC, had arrived at figures for the "obliquity of the ecliptic", the angle at which the Earth's axis is tilted with respect to the plane of its orbit around the Sun. Some, in Flamsteed's day, thought this angle was diminishing. The great Copernicus had been of this opinion but Flamsteed thought this idea was wrong. He believed he could reconcile all the different observations ever made by allowing for differences in atmospheric refraction depending on the latitude of the observer. By observing the Sun at its highest midday position on 11th June, 1690 and from a measurement of the latitude of Greenwich he had made in 1689 using the Mural Arc constructed by Abraham Sharp, Flamsteed determined the obliquity of the ecliptic as 23 degrees 29 minutes 24 seconds. Actually, the angle is very slowly decreasing by an almost imperceptible 0.47 seconds of arc each year and in the year 2000 will be about 23 degrees 26 minutes 34 seconds, so the measurement which Flamsteed made in 1690 was very close indeed to the exact value for that date.

A further parameter of the skies, which had been discovered by Hipparchus during the second century before Christ and which Flamsteed verified by measurement, is known as the "precession of the equinoxes". This has the effect of producing a gradual shifting of the constellations around the celestial sphere as the equinoxes move westward by about 50 seconds of arc each year. Although the effect was known to the ancient Greeks it was only explained by Newton's gravitational theory. It is caused by the attraction of the Sun and Moon on the equatorial bulge of the Earth, with the Moon being responsible for about two-thirds of the effect. Just as a gyroscope changes the direction of its axis when given a push on its circumference and tilts at 90 degrees to the applied force, so the Earth's axis tilts under the gravitational influences of the Sun and Moon. This is a very slow effect, however and needs comparison of the position of stars some centuries apart to determine it with any accuracy. Hipparchus used star positions taken 150 years earlier than his own day to compare with his own measurements and produced a figure of 46 seconds of arc for the annual precessional change over that period. Flamsteed took the observations of Hipparchus and other ancient astronomers, together with his own sightings, to arrive at values of 51.0 and 49.7 seconds for the annual precession of the equinoxes - which are both very close to the figure 50.2 seconds which is generally accepted nowadays. Although Flamsteed did not appreciate the reason for this gradual precession he realised that it was a property of the skies which had occurred at roughly the same rate for the past 1800 years. It required the great genius of Sir Isaac Newton (who himself had a good knowledge of the work of the ancient Greeks as well as that of his contemporary John Flamsteed) to show that this hitherto mysterious effect was caused by the same kind of gravitational force which kept the Moon in its orbit, the planets in their wanderings and which governed the tracks of comets through the sky.

CHAPTER X

Further Work at Greenwich

It might have been thought that the Astronomer Royal lived a rather lonely and isolated life at the observatory in Greenwich Park, being occupied with his observations and his instruments during the night and with his calculations of star positions from the raw observational data during the daytime. This, however, would be far from the truth. The work of John Flamsteed was not easy and he had many difficulties to contend with, the things he achieved being only obtained in his words "by labour harder than thrashing" (i.e. threshing the corn, which was of course a heavy manual task in Flamsteed's day). But in fact, the work of the observatory assistant was probably harder and received much less recognition than that of the astronomer in charge. About 100 years after Flamsteed's time at the observatory, Thomas Evans, who was an assistant from 1796 to 1798 wrote, "Nothing can exceed the tediousness and ennui of the life the assistant leads in this place, excluded from all society except, perhaps, that of a poor mouse....Here, forlorn, he spends days, weeks, months in the same wearisome computations, without a friend to shorten the tedious hours, or a soul with which he can converse..." A careful assistant, whose arithmetic was good, could relieve the astronomer of much of the tedious calculation which was necessary to reduce the raw observational data into an accurate star position. Each calculation would take over an hour to complete and Flamsteed tried to get each one performed by two independent persons as a check on each other. These persons were called "calculators". How their lives would have been improved had they had access to a modern electronic calculator or personal computer!

John Flamsteed himself, however, was not a solitary person, seeking the seclusion of his observatory and shunning contact with the outside world, as some have supposed. He was in touch with many sailors and merchants both in London and in other places. He purchased lenses and various pieces of equipment on behalf of his friends from craftsmen in London and in return had the assistance of friends in other places, such as Paris, where Charles Towneley, brother of Richard Towneley, was often on business. It might be thought that the delivery of small packages from Europe, before the era of modern postal services, would be a problem but Flamsteed wrote to Towneley, "As for conveyance, I know none better than by our yachts. The captains are all my neighbours and ready to do me whatever kindness I desire. They are often going over to Dieppe, whither I suppose your brother may easily get any box conveyed. I shall discourse the captains - I doubt not but we may receive them safe." Flamsteed was thus well known to the captains of small boats in the Channel, who would come to harbour at Greenwich and he was well respected by them.

He was also in touch with numerous correspondents both in Britain and overseas. These varied from famous men like Newton, Halley and Cassini, to sea-captains who wished to improve their knowledge of navigation and to amateur astronomers like the apothecary William Bossley in Bakewell, Derbyshire. It is said that Flamsteed was in correspondence with 75 persons at one time, who wished to benefit from the skill and experience of the royal astronomer at Greenwich. He was a source of information to all who wrote to him and was not reticent or reluctant to divulge his opinions on astronomical matters or to give out data, providing he knew that this was as accurate as he could possibly make it. If his figures were not sufficiently accurate, then Flamsteed did not like to have them published or distributed widely as he knew this would only invite criticism - and like most men of his day, he tended to resent criticism, though he was ready to criticise others if their published work failed to meet his own standards. Flamsteed also took an active part in the work of the Royal Society after his election as a Fellow on 8th February, 1677 and altogether he published 46 papers in the *Philosophical Transactions of the Royal Society*. He served on the Council of the Society from November 1681 to 1684 and again from November 1698 to 1700, so in no way could he be considered as a reclusive figure. The name of John Flamsteed became internationally famous throughout Europe because of his publications in the scientific literature of the day and his correspondence with the principal observatories on the continent.

Visitors sought out Flamsteed from far and wide, so much so that he began to regard some of these as a waste of his precious time. One visitor, however, was quite exceptional. When Peter the Great, Emperor of Russia, visited England in 1698, he specially asked to see the Observatory because of its international fame. He saw Flamsteed and his assistants performing their work and became so interested in what they were doing that he came back on three further occasions to find out more about the measurements they were carrying out and the instruments they employed, so that he could set up similar facilities in Russia.

One particular phenomenon that Flamsteed discussed in correspondence with others was atmospheric refraction - an important topic since the majority of observations, except for those taken of objects nearly overhead, needed correction for this angular distortion brought about by the Earth's atmosphere. Tycho Brahe seems to have been the first to allow for atmospheric refraction when measuring the altitude of stars or planets near the horizon, making a correction of 34 minutes of arc for the Sun, 33 minutes for the Moon and 30 minutes for the stars. Since the apparent diameter of the Sun or Moon is about 30 minutes of arc, Tycho was the first astronomer to appreciate that when these are rising or setting we can actually see them at times when in fact they are below the horizon (see figure 12b).

In his lectures, Flamsteed likened the atmosphere to water in a deep vessel which enables a coin placed on the bottom to become visible to the eye which peers over the vessel's edge (see figure 12a). He considered that refraction in the atmosphere is due to water vapour rather than to the air itself and suggested that the morning refraction could exceed that in the evening due to the increased moisture then in the air - which was later dispersed by the Sun. The variability of refraction from one day to another was also put down to the presence of varying degrees of dampness in the air.

Atmospheric Refraction

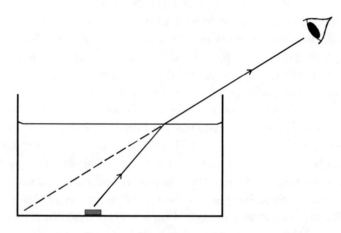

Figure 12a.
Flamsteed's illustration of refraction, showing how water in a deep vessel enables a coin, otherwise hidden by the vessel's edge, to become visible.

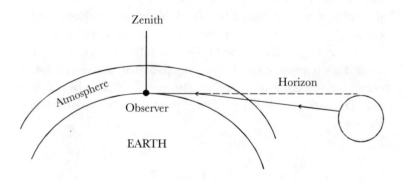

Figure 12b.
Refraction due to the Earth's atmosphere enables the Sun to be seen when actually it lies just below the horizon. Tycho Brahe seems to have been the first person to appreciate this fact.

Johannes Kepler attempted the scientific measurement and explanation of atmospheric refraction, showing that the angle of refraction depends on the angle of incidence but it was left to the Dutch astronomer and mathematician, Willibrord Snell, to enunciate the law which governs refraction. Kepler was puzzled that water shows no change of refraction with depth, whereas the atmosphere appears to do so. He, along with others, visualised a uniform atmosphere about 2.5 miles thick surrounding the Earth.

John Flamsteed appreciated that lighter components of the atmosphere would rise higher than the denser components and therefore he concluded that the density of the atmosphere would increase down to ground level. This, of course, was before Newton's theory of gravity was published, and Flamsteed's ideas were based on experiments with the mercury barometer which had been invented in 1641 by the Italian, Toricelli. During the time he had lived in Derby, Flamsteed had carried a mercury barometer from the base to the top of the tower of All Saints Church (now known as Derby Cathedral) and had noted that the level of the mercury had fallen by 0.14 inches as he climbed a height of 142 feet. He corresponded with his friend Richard Towneley on the subject of the variation of pressure with altitude, and encouraged him to take readings with a mercury barometer as he ascended the 1,929 foot Pendle Hill near his home in Lancashire. Flamsteed also corresponded with Isaac Newton on the subject and in November 1694 Newton sent Flamsteed a comprehensive table of corrections to be applied to observations at various angles above the horizon at different seasons of the year. This is reproduced below, together with a modern list of corrections (taken from *Astronomy: Principles and Practice*, by A E Roy and D Clarke, 2nd edition 1982, published by Adam Hilger, Bristol).

Angle Above Horizon	Isaac Newton's Suggested Correction			Modern Correction Value
	Summer	Spring/Autumn	Winter	
0	31'30"	33'20"	35'10"	35'21"
3	12'52"	13'40"	14'28"	14'24"
6	7'24"	7'52"	8'20"	
10	4'36"	4'53"	5'10"	5'18"
20	2'17"	2'25"	2'33"	
30	1'26"	1'31"	1'36"	1'41"
60		0'30"		0'34"

Table allowing correction for atmospheric refraction

Newton suggested that Flamsteed should note the air temperature and pressure when he made observations so that he might correct for atmospheric refraction more accurately but Flamsteed, perhaps influenced by the fact that for many years he had lived overlooking the mists on the Thames from Greenwich Hill, supposed that dampness in the air might be a greater factor and therefore he seems to have ignored Newton's advice.

The change of air pressure with height above sea level, or how the atmosphere thins out above the Earth's surface, continued to be a subject of great scientific interest for over a hundred years after Flamsteed's time. Thus, when Dr. Michel-Gabriel Paccard made the first ascent of Mont Blanc, in 1786, he took with him a mercury barometer and made measurements at various stages of the climb. Mont Blanc is 4,807 metres (15,771 feet) high and the presence of breathable air at that altitude finally silenced those who believed that the Earth's atmosphere vanished about 2.5 miles above sea level.

Another topic that Flamsteed discussed was the cause of the twinkling of the stars and he attributed this to variations in the atmosphere. He noticed that a finely graduated calibration strip placed 300 yards from a 14 foot telescope could not be read in bright sunlight due to the agitation of the air but when a cloud obstructed the sun the scale could easily be read. He thought that the twinkling of stars could be due to changes in Earth's atmosphere at great heights. Similarly, he considered that the shimmering observed as the Sun was setting was due to the agitation of the air through which the light rays travelled. At sunset these rays travel a longer distance through the atmosphere, producing the shimmering effect but when the Sun is overhead the light passes through a thinner section of the atmosphere and shimmering is not seen.

Further collaboration between Newton and Flamsteed followed Newton's request for information on the apparent diameters of the planets when they were at their greatest and least distances from Earth. This gave Newton information about the orbits of the planets which must have been useful when he was working on his gravitational theory, leading up to the publication of his *Principia* in 1687. Flamsteed was also engaged in careful observations of the four known satellites of Jupiter and provided Newton with data on the diameters of these satellites - although he told Newton it was impossible to be certain concerning such small objects at such a large distance from Earth. He suggested that if the radius of Jupiter were 1000 units, the diameters of the satellites could be, the 1st [Io] 46 units, 2nd [Europa] 40, 3rd [Ganymede] 53, and the 4th [Callisto] 25 - figures which were remarkably accurate for the two inner satellites but astray on the other two. The apparent radius of Jupiter occupies some 24 seconds of arc and the satellites, therefore, have diameters of around one second. Flamsteed probably used a 16 foot telescope fitted with a micrometer which had more than 3000 divisions per inch for these observations but we can appreciate why he told Newton that his readings were not to be relied upon.

Another question from Newton (August 10th, 1691) concerned any colour change that might occur when a satellite of Jupiter was occulted by the planet. Perhaps Newton was wondering about different speeds for red and blue light which might become apparent as these rays travelled the huge distance from the planet. He had already discovered the spectral composition of white light and knew that light had a finite speed - since this had been explained by Romer on his visit to Greenwich when Newton had been present. Romer had explained variations in the times of eclipse of Jupiter's satellite Io when the planet was at different distances from the Earth as being due to the speed of light, which his observations had indicated was about 140,000 miles per second. Flamsteed replied to Newton saying that he was unable to detect any obvious change in colour as the satellite was eclipsed but that there was a gradual dimming of the satellite rather than an abrupt disappearance.

Flamsteed also supplied Newton with some 150 observed positions of the Moon, in order that he could calculate its orbit accurately but this data was insufficient for his needs. He pressed Flamsteed for more observations but Flamsteed replied that he was not able to devote the time which the work would entail to this task, particularly as the request came at a time when he was suffering worse than usual health. It was at this point that a definite cooling off in the relationship between these two men commenced, leading gradually towards their barely concealed hostility. This was a great pity as they had so much to offer each other in the way of collaboration. Flamsteed was undoubtedly the most accurate observer of his time with a wealth of astronomical data in his possession, whereas Newton possessed unique mathematical ability and the two men were ideally placed for effective mutual progress. It seems that Flamsteed considered he received little credit for the valuable information he supplied to Newton and which was vital for Newton's published work. On the other hand, Newton was impatient at the slow rate at which the Moon data were being gathered (which was one of the principal purposes for which the Royal Observatory had been set up) and he believed that Flamsteed was missing an unequalled opportunity of solving the problems posed by the Moon's orbit. A little later, in 1698, Newton heard that Flamsteed had submitted a paper for publication *On the Parallax of Earth's Annual Orb*, in which it was mentioned that Newton was working on a theory of the Moon using Flamsteed's observations as raw data. Newton took great exception to this premature disclosure of his work, which was very difficult and might be unsuccessful in the end and he wrote to Flamsteed, in January 1699, protesting at this indiscretion. Newton had been appointed by the king as Warden of the Mint in 1696 and he said that he might be accused of neglecting the king's business and trifling with mathematical theories instead if Flamsteed's announcement of his work were published. Flamsteed was probably shocked by the obvious indignation shown by Newton, a man whom he held in high regard both as a scientist and also as a theologian and he quickly wrote to cancel this paragraph from his paper because it had offended Newton. He also wrote a rather conciliatory letter to Newton, saying that research into the things of nature could surely never be interpreted as "trifling with mathematics". He said, "The works of the Eternal Providence I hope will be a little better understood through your labours and mine than they were formerly". Perhaps this smoothed things over for a time but the good relationship between these two men, each outstanding in their different capabilities, was never the same again.

Another topic on which Flamsteed and Newton had collaborated earlier was that concerning the movement of comets through the heavens. Flamsteed had noticed that a comet in 1677 had appeared in the same place as earlier comets in 1653 and 1665, and he suggested that possibly these could be reappearances of the same object - at that time a revolutionary idea as almost everyone believed that comets travelled in straight lines - but his suggestion was firmly rejected by Newton. Another bright, rapidly moving comet was discovered by Gottfreid Kirch of Coburg, Germany, in November 1680. Flamsteed first observed this "Great Comet" before sunrise during November and noted that on December 11th it could be seen from Greenwich before the morning twilight ended. In the head of the comet Flamsteed noted "a dull star, much less than Jupiter, not round but like a square with the sharp corners rudely rubbed off". It was then three degrees above the horizon and Flamsteed's measurements suggested 9th December for its closest distance to the Sun, and he thought that on December 12th it was as far from Earth as was the Sun. In the early part of 1681 another comet appeared, which was carefully observed by Newton in Cambridge as well as by Flamsteed at Greenwich. Newton diligently plotted the path of this comet until it became too faint to be seen through his telescope on 9th March, 1681.

John Flamsteed thought that these appearances were of one and the same comet, which had changed direction when it came near the Sun due to some magnetic effect, such as a change in its polarity, producing first an attraction and later a repulsion from the Sun. Newton discounted Flamsteed's interpretation because he could not envisage how a body as hot as the Sun could be magnetic, seeing that heating to only a dull red heat destroys the magnetism of an iron bar. Also, he was searching for an explanation of the paths of comets based on his theory of gravitation. Some four years later he agreed with Flamsteed that only one comet was involved and in his *Principia* of 1687 he argued that a parabolic path for this comet of 1680-1681 would fit all the observations quite well. However, Newton failed to acknowledge that it was Flamsteed who had first suggested a curved path for the comet - which quite naturally made Flamsteed very annoyed.

Edmond Halley was in France in the early part of 1681, visiting the Paris Observatory and on January 22nd he sent Flamsteed some observations of the comet made in France and asked for Flamsteed's thoughts on the general nature of comets. Flamsteed appears to be reasonably friendly towards Halley at this point, although relations between the two were deteriorating and afterwards broke out into open hostility. He replied on February 17th, first pointing out that he had noticed a difference of 4 or 5 minutes of arc in the position of the comet reported from Paris as compared with his own observations, which he suspected was due to the Paris observatory using Tycho's incorrect star positions as references. Flamsteed preferred his own readings of star positions...naturally! He went on to say that there had only been one comet, which had come from the north, crossed the ecliptic and headed towards the Sun following a curved path. He believed that the Sun attracted all heavenly bodies according to their "different substance" and their distance from the Sun; ideas which Isaac Newton later explained by his theory of gravity. The tail of a comet was formed, Flamsteed wrote, by the humid atmosphere generated by heat when it came near the Sun. This "steam" would be propelled large distances through space "causing the tail to double in length when nearest the Sun to what it was at perigee when it was more easily observed". The deflection of the comet's tail was like "smoke from a chimney on a moving ship, or the steam from a drop of water falling onto a moving hot iron". In return for these observations, Flamsteed asked Halley to let him know about the work of the Paris Observatory and its instruments.

Newton had suggested that planets gradually increase in mass by acquisitions from the tails of comets but Flamsteed disagreed with this notion. Halley tended to support Newton's idea and said that Saturn moved more slowly than it had done 100 years before due to its increased mass. Flamsteed reasoned that Saturn must therefore have moved further away from the Sun, which he thought was unlikely and his own measurements showed that Saturn moved no more slowly in his day than it had done 2,000 years before. He therefore concluded that planets gain no appreciable mass from the tails of comets - a view that is confirmed nowadays when it is known that comets are quite small and very light compared to the planets and any accretion from comets would not significantly affect a planet's mass or its orbit. Little more was learnt about the physical structure or composition of comets until the second half of the 19th Century - some two hundred years after Flamsteed had ventured his opinion on the nature of comets.

Edmond Halley was fascinated by comets and he became keenly interested in another bright one (later to become famous as Halley's Comet) which was seen in 1682. Halley was a very capable mathematician and he was eager to calculate the path of this comet - for which he required Flamsteed's accurate observations. He thought he would be unlikely to succeed if he asked Flamsteed directly for his observations, because of Flamsteed's increasing opposition to him and therefore, he took a more circuitous route for the desired information. He asked his great friend Newton to obtain Flamsteed's data. He told Newton that he badly needed this information to support his belief that the comet of 1682 moved in a closed orbit and had been seen three times previously since 1531. Newton realised the scientific importance of Halley's idea and so he obtained the required data from Flamsteed and passed it on. Halley was then able to confirm that the comet travelled in an elliptical orbit with a period of about 76 years and he predicted its reappearance in 1758. When this prediction was duly fulfilled, long after Halley's death, the comet was named Halley's Comet and it has continued to reappear at regular intervals until its most recent visit in 1985-86. Few people nowadays however, remember that it was only the careful observations of John Flamsteed that enabled Halley to make this remarkable prediction. Halley himself recognised the high quality of Flamsteed's work and praised him for its accuracy but the animosity which arose between these two men lasted for the rest of Flamsteed's life.

When Flamsteed published his work *On the Parallax of Earth's Annual Orb* he reported his observations made over a period of eight years on the difference in angle between the Pole Star and the true geographic north pole, saying that he found this difference to be greater at intervals of six months when the Earth would be at opposite sides of its annual orbit. He interpreted this fact as an annual parallax variation of about 40 - 45 seconds of arc, due to viewing the star from different locations as the Earth orbited the Sun. In this interpretation he was mistaken, since the greatest annual parallax for the nearest star, Proxima Centauri, is only 0.76 seconds of arc. What Flamsteed observed was explained by James Bradley - the third Astronomer Royal at Greenwich from 1742 to 1762 - as the aberration of light, which has the effect of changing the apparent angle of a star by 41 seconds of arc over a six-month period.

This is an effect in some ways rather similar to our common experience of seeing raindrops, which are actually falling vertically to the ground, apparently slanting at an angle when viewed from the side window of a moving car. The faster the car moves, the greater this angle will be, and when the speed of the car equals that at which the raindrops are falling to earth the angle will be 45 degrees to vertical. Likewise the umbrella of a rapidly moving person in vertically falling rain must be tilted towards the direction of travel (see figure 11a) if it is to provide cover over all the body. In the case of light, the photons of which can be considered to be like very small raindrops, the effect is due to the speed of the Earth in its orbit relative to the speed of light from a distant star, as illustrated in figure 11b. Suppose that light from a star which is vertically overhead, enters the objective of the telescope at A, travelling vertically downwards with speed "c". At the same time the Earth's orbital motion is carrying the telescope sideways with speed "v". In order for the light photons to pass down the telescope without colliding with the sides, the telescope must be tilted at a small angle * to the vertical and the light will emerge from the eye-piece at B. In the time taken for light to travel vertically from A to D, the eye-piece will have moved horizontally from B to D. The angle * will be calculated from the ratio of these distances, which is the same as the ratio of the speed of the telescope to that of light, or

$$\tan * = BD/AD = v/c$$

At intervals of six months the Earth will be at opposite sides of its orbit, travelling in opposite directions. Thus, the star overhead will appear to shift through a total angle of 2* in this period.

If Flamsteed had comprehended this reason for the angular difference he had observed, he would have been able to calculate the speed of light in an alternative way to that of Romer - which was based on the variation in the times of eclipse of Jupiter's satellite Io. Also it would have provided direct evidence for the revolution of the Earth around the Sun, thus confirming the Copernican theory and the name of Flamsteed would have won permanent fame. Unfortunately, he failed to appreciate this consequence of the finite speed of light, though it should be remembered that other brilliant men of the time, such as Newton and Halley, also missed this explanation of Flamsteed's observation. It was left for James Bradley, another astronomer after the pattern of Flamsteed with a passion for accurate measurements on stars which were nearly overhead, to announce the correct explanation for this apparent change in position with time, in the year 1728.

Another opportunity that Flamsteed missed, which would have secured his immortality amongst astronomers, was when he misinterpreted his observation of the faint and slow-moving planet (later called Uranus) in 1690, mistaking this for a star of the 6th magnitude in the constellation Taurus. Altogether some 19 further observations of Uranus were made by different astronomers, who all recorded it as a 6th or 7th magnitude star, before Sir William Herschel in 1781 finally identified it as a planet. Herschel used a high quality reflector telescope of 6 inches diameter at his home in Bath and thought at first that he had seen either "a nebulous star or a comet". However, subsequent movement of the object showed it to be a new planet - the first to be discovered since prehistoric times. Caroline Herschel, Sir William's sister and a fine astronomer in her own right, used Flamsteed's star catalogue as reference for her own observations and she recalculated all Flamsteed's star positions from his original data, publishing a small *errata* listing all his mistakes. She found that Flamsteed had probably observed the remote and slowly moving planet Uranus on about six occasions between 1690 and 1715 but on each occasion he had recorded it as a star of the 6th or 7th magnitude. This was a great opportunity which Flamsteed missed but of course, in his day all astronomers believed that only five planets existed in the heavens and that these had all been known since ancient times. They were not expecting to find any new planets and therefore, it is not really surprising that they failed to do so.

CHAPTER XI

The "Pirated" Version of Flamsteed's Work, 1712

From ancient times astronomers had looked up into the heavens and discerned there the patterns of stars which formed the various constellations. Artists had drawn conceptual pictures of each constellation, using their imagination to fill out the missing detail in many cases and it was possible to identify a small location in the night sky by referring for instance to "the eye of the Bull" or "the front paw of the Great Bear" or "the neck of the Whale". But by the 16th Century, it was felt that only by numerically recording the exact angular co-ordinates of each star would the constellations be sufficiently well defined for the use of astronomers, both at that time and in the future.

The greatest innovator in positional astronomy was the famous Tycho Brahe (1546-1601), who built a magnificent observatory called Uraniborg and employed large and expensive equipment, such as the sextant, to measure the angular distance between stars. The work of Tycho was much admired by John Flamsteed, even though Tycho still clung to the ancient belief that the Earth was at the centre of all things. He envisaged a complicated system in which the Moon circled close to the Earth, whilst further away the Sun, surrounded by circling planets, also orbited the Earth. Also, although Tycho was a careful and accurate observer, he lived before the invention of the telescope and all his sightings of stars and subsequent calculations of their positions on the hemisphere of the sky were naked eye observations. Tycho logged the positions of 777 stars, but unfortunately died suddenly before his work was printed. His star catalogue was eventually published by Christianus Longomontanus in 1622 as *Astronomia Danica* and was again published, after expansion to over a thousand stars, by his young colleague Johannes Kepler in the *Rudolphine Tables* of 1627. These were the best star catalogues available in the first half of the 17th Century.

By the 1670s, the Polish astronomer Johannes Hevelius, who worked in Danzig (modern Gdansk) had become famous as one who plotted the positions of stars with great accuracy (as well as being one of the earliest compilers of an atlas of the Moon). His work on the stars was also based only on naked eye sightings and Robert Hooke in particular criticised it fiercely, claiming it was only a slight improvement on the data of Tycho because Hevelius had failed to make use of the telescope as a sighting device. Both Tycho and Hevelius could fix star positions to about one minute of arc, or around 1/30th of the Moon's diameter, which might have been thought accurate enough. But Hooke and Flamsteed both knew that by using a telescope with cross-wires as a sight, much more accurate numerical data on star positions could be achieved. John Flamsteed, with his knowledge and skill in using the screw micrometer fitted at the prime focus of his telescope, realised that very small angles could be accurately measured. He made it his life's ambition to chart the sky with unprecedented accuracy, so that all who came after him might use his records and rely on his work as a standard of reference.

Because Flamsteed was such a perfectionist, he was not really satisfied with publishing preliminary results or giving data for only some of the constellations. He had the burning ambition to map all the constellations visible in the northern sky, though he knew this would be a life-long task. So, although he was quite willing to provide Sir Isaac Newton, Edmond Halley, or any other of his colleagues with a limited range of observations which he considered were accurate, he worked towards the eventual publication of a fully complete star catalogue.

But as Flamsteed grew older, Newton in particular became eager to see all the results of the Royal Observatory at Greenwich published, so that these would be readily available to all astronomers and scientists. Newton was aware that Tycho had died suddenly at the early age of 54 years and more than twenty years had then passed before his work was made available generally. Furthermore, Newton was some years older than Flamsteed and probably he was keen to gain access to the accurate observations performed at Greenwich so that he could use these in his own theoretical work during the time that was left to him.

Flamsteed, however, was irritated by the pressures put upon him to publish his still incomplete star catalogue. Probably only he realised what a huge amount of work was involved in making observations of sufficient accuracy and then reducing the raw data, with corrections for all kinds of instrument inaccuracies and atmospheric refraction, so that a true positional record was made. Each observation required over an hour's calculation, during which arithmetical errors could easily be made. Flamsteed wrote to Sir Christopher Wren complaining about the pressures being heaped upon him and the questions of those who continually asked him when the work would be completed. He commented, "They might as well ask why St. Paul's Cathedral is not yet finished!" One can see that Flamsteed visualised his star catalogue as a great work of reference for all time, and something that could not be compromised by undue haste.

Newton had been Lucasian professor at Cambridge when Flamsteed first registered as a sudent there. Afterwards Newton became a valued colleague of Flamstead and benefited from his observations of the stars and planets and the 1680 comet. Flamsteed had initially looked upon Newton with great respect and valued his friendship both as a scientist and a man of God. He wrote, "Mr. Newton's approbation is more to me than the cry [or flattering praise] of all the ignorant in the world". However, he believed that Newton, although he had briefly acknowledged his observations in the *Principia*, had not really given him the full credit he deserved, since much of Newton's work on gravity had been founded upon the practical work undertaken by Flamsteed. He began to feel suspicious that Newton was obtaining fame and international importance largely as a result of the data he supplied him with and little credit was reflected back to him for such data. It seems highly probable that at this time Newton never intended to belittle the contribution which Flamsteed had made but he was rather thoughtless about the feelings of his colleague and preoccupied in his mind as he concentrated on the difficult theoretical work he was undertaking.

Newton was the supreme mathematical physicist of the time, whilst Flamsteed was the most careful practical astronomer. Their work should have dovetailed nicely and been mutually beneficial. Unfortunately, a feeling of distrust developed instead and their co-operation became strained. Flamsteed told Newton that his raw data needed a considerable amount of correction before they could be reduced to useful positional observations and that a considerable amount of mathematical work was involved. Newton, the incomparable mathematician, replied that he was interested only in "your observations, not your calculations" obviously believing that if he had access to Flamsteed's uncorrected data he could produce better calculated results, or more readily find out where things were going wrong in his theory. This rather abrupt dismissal of his mathematics made the Astronomer Royal even more inclined to the view that he was being undervalued and the tension between himself and Newton mounted.

Flamsteed attempted to provide any enquirer with accurate positional information which he himself had corrected for instrument errors, atmospheric refraction, etc. He alone knew the experimental errors involved in his measurements and how to correct for them. For instance, Flamsteed knew that the screw-threads which moved his telescopic sights were not perfectly cut and he devised a correction table which gave the accurate angle for any marked place on the circumference of the dial which read out the angular position. Capable mathematicians like Newton, Gregory, or Halley, without reference to this correction table, would naturally assume that the screw-threads were accurately cut and in recalculating Flamsteed's results they would find discrepancies which they might consider were due to his careless arithmetic. In fact, they would themselves introduce errors and produce erroneous results because they had neglected this correction for experimental error. The proper calculation of a star's position from the raw data was a most tedious and time-consuming task, requiring a knowledge of all the experimental errors together with great patience and concentration rather than advanced mathematics.

After Newton was appointed Warden of the Mint in the spring of 1696, he moved from Cambridge to live in Jermyn Street, London, and he was then able to visit the Greenwich Observatory more frequently and to attend more meetings of the Royal Society. His queries to Flamsteed about the publication of his results became more insistent. Although Flamsteed wished to see his observations printed, he required time to achieve the degree of accuracy which he thought was necessary and he required more "calculators" to assist with the reduction of his raw data. With the backing of the Royal Society in 1704, Sir Isaac Newton, now their President, approached Prince George of Denmark, Consort to Queen Anne, to ask for special funding so that the publication of nearly 30 years work of the Royal Observatory could go ahead. Prince George had recently been made a Fellow of the Royal Society and he agreed to provide the money as his personal contribution to what he thought would be a landmark in British science. Flamsteed estimated that the star catalogue with all the other items he planned to accompany it would run to about 1,400 pages and a committee of the Royal Society was set up to administer the allocated sum of around £1,200. This committee included Sir Isaac Newton, Sir Christopher Wren, Professor David Gregory, Dr. John Arbuthnot (who was physician to the Royal Family), Edmond Halley, Dr. Sloane, Dr. Mead, Mr. Francis Robartes, M.P., and Mr. Hill - an impressive collection of prominent men. Unfortunately, a fundamental difference of opinion existed between this committee and John Flamsteed from the outset. They believed that all the data belonged to the Royal Observatory, a government institution and it was therefore public property, whereas Flamsteed was of the opinion that, as he had done the work and provided the scientific instruments, the data belonged to him.

With some misgivings, Flamsteed handed the manuscripts he had already checked for accuracy over to the committee, so that the first volume of his observations, those obtained by the use of his 7 ft sextant, could proceed. He understood that the finished books would become his property after a certain number had been distributed to the universities and to particular friends of Prince George. Also by agreement the committee would reimburse Flamsteed for any expenses incurred in employing additional assistants to recalculate and check the data ready for the printers. In 1705, Flamsteed gave Newton a further 175 handwritten pages of data which had been obtained using the mural arc constructed by Abraham Sharp. These sheets were incomplete and uncorrected, being intended only to show Flamsteed's intention to complete the work and to be preserved in case of accident or Flamsteed's premature death. The committee, who now called themselves the Referees, took these sheets and demanded all Flamsteed's remaining data without delay. The actual printing, however, proceeded only very slowly, for which Flamsteed was perhaps secretly grateful as it gave him more time to check his figures (whilst at the same time he could complain to the committee about the delay). Flamsteed was annoyed with the committee for continually pressing him for corrected data, which he could only produce at a pace which allowed him to ensure the utmost reliability in the work.

With the death of Prince George on October 28th, 1708, the printing press ground to a halt - amidst uncertainties about further funding. The first volume was completed, but the second of the intended volumes was barely started. Flamsteed looked upon this as a welcome interlude and heaved sighs of relief as the referees who were oppressing him appeared to have lost the authority derived from their royal patron. Nevertheless, he continued with his task of producing accurately calculated data, as well as increasing his stock of new observations. He was a dedicated observer who never ceased his practical work until a few days before his death.

The committee of referees had not forgotten their remit, however and they secured the backing of Queen Anne for their continued work. On March 14th, 1711, Dr. John Arbuthnot, who appeared to have taken on the role of secretary, wrote an official letter to John Flamsteed demanding all his papers under command of the queen. Publication had been arranged to proceed under the particular supervision of Sir Isaac Newton and Edmond Halley. This move seriously offended Flamsteed, who considered that the committee was "pirating" [or hi-jacking as we would say nowadays] his life's work and putting it into the hands of Newton, whom he had come to distrust and Halley, his sworn enemy. He protested to Dr. Arbuthnot that the data were his own property resulting from his own work over a period of 35 years, during which time he had worked day and night, in sickness and in health, largely at his own expense. He had spent over £2,000 of his own money in the work and now it seemed that it was to be stolen from him and given to those who did not understand the data and could not be trusted to print it properly. Flamsteed most likely had Halley in mind when he wrote this. He requested that he should scan and correct each page proof himself before the final printing was done, and if this were not allowed he would be forced to have the catalogue printed at his own expense as he could not bear to see his efforts ruined "and also the reputation of the Nation, Queen and People of Britain dishonoured". This appeal was ignored by Dr. Arbuthnot and the printing work went ahead. Flamsteed petitioned Queen Anne to stop the publication but she was probably anxious to get the work published, partly as a tribute to her late husband's memory. Flamsteed was a lone voice, opposed by the powerful committee of the Royal Society and all his protests went unheard.

It appears that Newton, at this time, was too busy and perhaps too old at 69 years of age to properly oversee the details of publishing and the younger man Halley had been given full power to go ahead as he thought fit. This was not unreasonable, since Halley had published a catalogue of stars of the southern hemisphere, based on his own observations, many years before. Also, he had been the prime mover in urging Newton to write his *Principia* and he had edited and paid for this outstanding book with his own money. Halley was, therefore, a man held in high esteem by his scientific colleagues and everyone supposed that he would be more than competent to oversee publication of the Greenwich data. However, much of the data seized from Flamsteed had not been checked for errors and was not in the correct final form. Halley used his own very considerable knowledge of astronomy and mathematics to bring the information into a usable state; he recalculated some of Flamsteed's work and did the best job he could. But only Flamsteed fully understood how the data had been obtained and how it needed to be corrected and the final work which was printed left much to be desired.

Flamsteed was enraged when finally, in 1712, a copy of this *Historia Coelestis libri duo* was sent to him. He found many figures were erroneous, much of his data had been omitted altogether, information was garbled and the provisional data on the Moon which he had given to Newton in confidence and on the understanding they would not be released without Flamsteed's specific approval had also been printed. Furthermore, Halley had written a short preface to the work which Flamsteed considered was libellous. This preface was indeed very disparaging of Flamsteed's contributions to astronomy, whilst emphasising the work that Newton and Halley himself had done.

Flamsteed was portrayed as an ineffective worker who had taken many years to produce few results. Halley wrote, "Flamsteed had now enjoyed the title of Astronomer Royal for nearly 30 years but still nothing had yet emerged from the Observatory to justify all the equipment and expense, so that he seemed so far, only to have worked for himself or at any rate for a few of his friends, even if it was generally accepted that all these years had not been wasted and that the Greenwich papers had grown into no small a pile".

Flamsteed's data were also said by Halley to be of dubious reliability and the work of publication had been held up on this account. "The work went well and was on the point of seeing the light of day at last when the press had to stop as the catalogue of fixed stars was defective and lacked many constellations, as it had been handed over to the delegates with numerous imperfections." To one who had always taken so many pains to ensure that all his published figures were of the utmost accuracy, this statement by Halley would have raised Flamsteed's blood pressure to boiling point! And Flamsteed had not "handed over" the data - his work had been dragged from him under protest and printed largely without his supervision or approval.

Halley had furthermore indicated that Flamsteed was probably no longer up to the job of being Astronomer Royal, in view of his age and failing eyesight, but that he himself was more than capable of completing the publication. He wrote, "As Flamsteed kept his eyes, now less acute at his advanced age, intent on the ever-increasing phenomena of the stars, the task was given to Edmond Halley, LL.D., Savilian Professor of Geometry and thoroughly experienced in astronomy, of supplying what the rest of the edition lacked and seeing it through to completion." Of his own efforts Halley wrote: "Not infrequently he [Halley] had to correct and amend errors in the positions of fixed stars made through the fault of the writer [Flamsteed] or the computer and he had to fill in quite a few gaps." "He had to undertake a vast mass of trigonometry calculations." "Hence arose a further labour to extract the observations of individual planets, to assign them to their particular class, and in addition, to deduce the right ascensions and declinations from them." In such sentences as these, Halley made sure that his own contribution to the Greenwich star catalogue did not go unrecognised, whilst any inaccuracies would be considered to be those of Flamsteed which had escaped Halley's notice.

Halley possibly had some misgivings about his role as editor of this huge catalogue of astronomical information and perhaps felt that it was not as complete or reliable as it should have been despite all his efforts, for he wrote himself a kind of escape clause. "We decided not to publish all the observations we found." Also he concluded, "The odd blemish should not cause offence, nor the fact that so many printing errors are found in the first book... Flamsteed well understood the reasons for both. So that the excessive number of mistakes should not deter those wishing to use the observations, we have collected those noticed in a careful re-reading and which might be of some importance, and it should be no hardship for the kindly reader to correct them with his pen in the footnotes of the book where they are found."

When Flamsteed saw this published catalogue and read its preface, he recognised that his worst fears had become reality. His work, which he had intended should be a complete record of the stars with sufficient accuracy to stand for all time, had been printed with both errors and omissions. He considered it to be a travesty of all that he had aimed for during his occupation of the Royal Observatory. Whereas before he had mistrusted the Referees and had felt that any publication they made would fall far short of his own standard of perfection, he now realised that the final outcome was far worse than he had anticipated. He called Halley "a malicious thief" for stealing his life's work and corrupting it so badly in these volumes now printed. Although he had not been able to influence the Queen or the Royal Society to prevent the publication, or to secure himself the position of proof-reader before the final printing, Flamsteed now determined to publish his own correct version at his own expense so that his original intention would be carried out. Accordingly he wrote to Sir Isaac Newton asking for the return of his manuscripts. However, these were probably with Halley, as Newton seemed to have played little part in the details of either correcting, checking or printing the work. It seems that Flamsteed never obtained the return of some of his manuscripts, but as these had been copied from sheets still in Flamsteed's possession this was not an insuperable problem.

Flamsteed's great opportunity came following the death of Queen Anne on August 1st, 1714 and also that of the Earl of Halifax, Newton's chief supporter at the royal court, on May 19th, 1715. The country was thrown into something of a political turmoil over the matter of the succession since Queen Anne had no surviving children, and the Hanoverian King George I came to the throne. The new Lord Chamberlain knew John Flamsteed well and was well-disposed towards him, as was Sir Robert Walpole who was First Lord of the Treasury. With these friends now in positions of influence, Flamsteed petitioned the Lords of the Treasury for possession of the remaining unsold copies of the Greenwich star catalogue. His plea was upheld and they ordered that the 300 copies which had not already been distributed, out of the 400 printed, should be delivered to the Astronomer Royal at Greenwich. It must have been with great confusion and considerable loss of face that the former Referees complied with this command of the Court in March 1716.

On receiving the 300 "pirated" copies of his work, Flamsteed lost no time in disposing of them. Sending a few of them complete to his particular friends, with a covering letter to explain his objections to the catalogue, he cut out and saved the 97 pages which he had checked himself and was sure of, before burning the rest on a bonfire in Greenwich Park. This he said, was "a sacrifice to heavenly truth".

Flamsteed attempted to have the copies of the catalogue which had already been distributed withdrawn from circulation, since these had been published under his name but without his approval. Some copies had, however, already been distributed to continental libraries and observatories. Ten copies had gone "to those concerned in the impression" - that is, the Referees. Thirty copies had been deposited with the Treasury in London, and Sir Isaac Newton and Edmond Halley had each been given one copy. Two copies had been sent to John Flamsteed for his own use. Three copies had been sent to Italy for various observatories there and ten to Paris for distribution amongst members of the Royal Paris Observatory and the French Academy of Sciences. Further individual copies had been presented to the King of France and to two other Frenchmen, Monsieur Torcy and Monsieur Des Marets.

Even long after John Flamsteed's death, his wife Margaret attempted to get known copies removed from circulation. She wrote on 22nd March, 1726, to the Revd. Dr. Mather of Corpus Christi College, who was Vice-Chancellor of Oxford University, requesting that the copy which was in the Bodleian Library should be removed from the bookshelves, on the grounds that the information it contained was incorrect and did an injustice to the memory of her husband. The Vice-Chancellor appears not to have heeded her petition. The "pirated" edition of *Historia Coelestis* based on Flamsteed's observations, but published without his approval, still exists in the Bodleian Library. The complete Halley version of 1712 is, however, an exceedingly rare book!

CHAPTER XII

Flamsteed as Rector of Burstow

Burstow is a tiny village situated about 25 miles south of Greenwich and lies near Gatwick Airport in Surrey. The parish church, dedicated to St. Bartholomew, dates back at least as far as the year 1121. It has an unusual wooden tower topped by a cedar-shingled spire at the western end and an attractive old porch on the south side (see figure 13). The adjoining church lands were originally quite extensive and held by the archbishops of Canterbury until 1536, when possession passed to the Crown. Nomination to the church living was thereafter made by the Lord Chancellor. It was under Lord North's patronage in 1684 that John Flamsteed, having been ordained as a deacon back in 1675, was elevated to the priesthood and appointed rector of this parish - a reasonably desirable position for a Church of England clergyman, with glebe and tithes at Burstow worth around £153 annually.

Flamsteed's predecessor as Rector of Burstow had been the Revd. Ralph Cooke, DD, who had served the parish from 1637 to 1684 - performing an enormously long pastoral ministry of 47 years. Although John Flamsteed was still resident at Greenwich for most of the year and visited Burstow only occasionally, it was through the Burstow connection that he met his future wife. She was Margaret Cooke, granddaughter of the previous rector and they were married on the 23rd of October, 1692, when Margaret would have been about 22 years old. Flamsteed was 46 years of age at the time of his marriage and the couple never had children. Margaret Flamsteed took a considerable interest in her husband's work and became mathematically educated to a point where she could competently assist him in making observations.

John Flamsteed had always been of a religious turn of mind and even in his youth felt that he was more suited to the contemplation of the higher things of God rather than being actively involved in worldly affairs. In common with many other scientists of the time, Flamsteed believed that investigating natural phenomena was one aspect of learning about God.

The general population, too, was far more interested in religious matters then than nowadays and full attendance at church services on the Sabbath day was common. We should remember also that the Bible had been translated into the language of the ordinary Englishman during the past century or so and in 1611 the Authorized Version had received royal approval and was appointed to be read in all the English churches. (The Bible had already appeared in the Welsh language in 1588.)

Flamsteed and his scientific contemporaries would have been well aware of passages of scripture such as *Psalm 19*, verse 1,"The heavens declare the glory of God and the firmament sheweth his handywork." The Bible indicated that in observing the things of nature and seeking to understand them, the scientist was in a privileged position, as one who was looking into the mind of God who had created the universe and all things in it. Flamsteed would be familiar with passages in the New Testament such as *Romans* chapter 1, verse 20, "For the invisible things of Him from the creation of the world are clearly seen, being understood by the things that are made, even his eternal power and Godhead." And again, in the Old Testament, *Psalm 111*, verse 2, "The works of the Lord are great, sought out of all them that have pleasure therein." This search for an understanding of natural phenomena in Flamsteed's time was no mere labelling of the beautiful things of creation with a moral purpose or lesson - which might have been a comparatively easy and superficial descriptive task. It was rather the search for a real understanding of the way nature worked - a difficult undertaking which required the full use of the human intellect in every conceivable way. But the person pursuing such a quest for knowledge was in a fortunate and honourable calling as *Proverbs* chapter 25, verse 2, declared, "It is the glory of God to conceal a thing; but the honour of kings is to search out a matter."

Figure 13.
South Porch of the Church of St. Bartholomew, Burstow.

Such feelings about their work being an investigation into the mind and works of God were common amongst scientists in England at this time and Flamsteed assumed this standpoint as a basis for his work in astronomy. He was dedicated to the careful observation of the heavens and a thoughtful explanation of the phenomena he saw, using such skill in mathematics as he possessed.

This fitted in well with his position as a Protestant Church of England clergyman; one who was not bound by the traditional authoritative and dogmatic teaching of the Roman Catholic Church - which it retained from the Dark Ages well into the 17th Century. Flamsteed was no religious bigot however. His great friend, Richard Towneley, for instance, was from a long-standing Roman Catholic background and many of his correspondents in Europe were Roman Catholic astronomers.

From his knowledge of history gained from the Old Testament, Flamsteed reasoned that the Jews were the first astronomers because of the importance the observation of the New Moon played in their celebration of feast days. Furthermore he surmised that the Jews were the first to make sundials, seeing that King Ahaz of Judah possessed one of these, referred to in *Isaiah* chapter 38, verses 7-8, over 700 years before the birth of Christ. Also when the Israelites had been taken captive to Assyria under Tiglath Pileser in the 8th Century B.C. Flamsteed believed they had taught astronomy to their Assyrian captors in order to gain more favourable treatment. Again, when the Kingdom of Judah was conquered around 586 B.C. and the Jews taken captive into Babylon during Nebuchadnezzar's reign, he believed they had passed on their knowledge of astronomy to the Babylonians - including knowledge of the 18 years 10 days Saros Cycle which enabled them to forecast eclipses. Similarly, knowledge of astronomy had passed to the Egyptian priests from Jews living in Egypt and subsequently the knowledge of astronomy and geometry had spread to Greece and into Europe through Thales of Miletus.

The 17th Century was a difficult period for the clergy, in that a struggle for political power between Roman Catholic and Protestant factions lay just below the surface of society and churchmen had to be rather careful not to show too much preference one way or the other. The men who translated the Bible sought the approbation and patronage of King James I (King James VI of Scotland) for their labours and in presenting their work to the king they steered a middle course between the extremists of both Roman Catholic and Nonconformist parties. In their preface to the Authorized Version, they declared, "So that if, on the one side, we shall be traduced by Popish Persons at home or abroad, who therefore will malign us because we are poor instruments to make God's holy truth to be yet more and more known unto the people, whom they desire still to keep in ignorance and darkness; or if, on the other side, we shall be maligned by self-conceited Brethren, who run their own ways and give liking unto nothing but what is framed by themselves, and hammered on their anvil; we may rest secure, supported within by the truth and innocency of a good conscience, having walked the ways of simplicity and integrity, as before the Lord; and sustained without by the powerful protection of Your Majesty's grace and favour, which will ever give countenance to honest and Christian endeavours against bitter censures and uncharitable imputations." John Flamsteed also followed a similar middle course during his tenure of office as Rector of Burstow.

Flamsteed was ordained during the reign of King Charles II and as a Protestant member of the Church of England he adopted a central position in the struggle between Roman Catholic "Popish Persons" and Nonconformist "self-conceited Brethren" in the extremist wings of the Church. In particular, after his appointment as Rector of Burstow, he was concerned not to allow the parish to swing one way or the other in respect of the High and Low Church practices which existed within the Church of England. This could have been difficult for him, as he was largely an absentee parson who relied on his local chaplain to carry out the regular routine of parish duties throughout most of the year. He could easily have lost touch with his parishioners in the village and found them inclining to one side or the other under the influence of a partisan local chaplain. In fact, some deviance from the middle course seemed to be threatening the stability of the parish when Flamsteed made his usual summer visit to Burstow in 1715 and found things not to his liking. By now, he was getting on in years and could, in view of his age and bodily infirmities, have been disposed to let things take their own course. But he was concerned about the way his parish was run and after 31 years as rector he still maintained his command of its affairs and wished to retain its middle-of-the-road position.

After his return from Burstow in October 1715, he wrote to

his friend and former colleague Abraham Sharp, "I resided at Burstow very uneasily, by reason I found my curate had signalized himself in such a manner for High Church that I was forced to dismiss him. I have not got another, and find it very difficult to get one that is not tainted by the same principles. This has caused me some journeys extraordinary to London and I fear will do more." This episode shows that Flamsteed was not afraid to take decisive action when he saw parish affairs going astray and, despite the extra work and travelling which this had entailed, he had dismissed the curate who inclined towards practices more like those associated with Roman Catholicism.

Flamsteed was also capable of standing his ground and taking a position equidistant from extremes on political questions - which were fairly closely related to religious attitudes in his day. For instance, in the year 1700, it was publicly reported that Flamsteed had adopted the Parliamentarian standpoint and had "justified the murder" of King Charles I - that unfortunate monarch who had been beheaded for treason back in 1649. The events leading up to the death of the king had taken place before Flamsteed was three years old and therefore unable to understand anything about the issues involved, much less to influence them. But Royalist and Parliamentarian sympathies lay buried only just below the surface for several decades after the king's execution and it seems that some of Flamsteed's detractors sought to ruin his reputation in the eyes of contemporary royal authority, which was of Stuart ancestry. Flamsteed firmly denied any suggestion of anti-royalist feelings, stating that, "He must certainly be a wicked man that would justify any murder whatsoever, be the person murdered never so bad. If they had said that I had vindicated the king's trial or execution it had been enough, but that looked not so black as murder." In fact, Flamsteed continued, "I am of the opinion that neither the Rump Parliament nor the High Commission Court had any right to judge the king." The downfall of King Charles I was brought about he said, "not by a party of ill subjects in his own kingdom alone, but by French contrivances that excited the rebellion, and by suggestions to his Queen [Henrietta Maria, who was the sister of the French King Louis XIII], and her ascendancy over him, that kept him from following those good counsels that were given him by the wisest of his peers and the best of his clergy about him." Obviously Flamsteed would not have jeopardised his position at the Royal Observatory or been disloyal to the patronage that had been extended to him during the reign of Charles II, but links with the early Stuarts were now becoming rather tenuous and Flamsteed was not under direct threat from the Royal Family when he stated these views on the king's execution and therefore he no doubt gave his honest opinion on the matter. If he had been strongly anti-royalist, this sentiment might have been expected to have been even more powerful in his youthful years and it is unlikely he would have become Astronomer Royal.

Although John Flamsteed was an absentee from his parish for most of the year, this did not mean that he took his church responsibilities lightly. It was quite common at that time for absentee rectors to be appointed in countryside parishes far from their usual place of residence and one of the most important tasks they had to oversee was the collection of tithes into the church and the administration of glebe lands. It was in connection with the annual tithes that Flamsteed regularly visited Burstow in July and August when the harvests were being reaped. He was well acquainted with farming and the affairs of the countryside from his roots in Derbyshire and the parishes of Burstow and Denby were probably not dissimilar from a farming point of view. So he was well fitted for a rural parish and was unlikely to allow any tenant farmer to get away with not paying his appropriate tithe to the church.

The curate who looked after routine matters in the parish was paid £40 per year by Flamsteed and this gives some comparison between the salary enjoyed by the Astronomer Royal (£100 per annum) and that of a lowly parish priest in those days. No doubt the curate would also receive sundry gifts in kind from his parishioners which would be a welcome help with his living costs. In one letter which still exists, Flamsteed advised his curate, Mr. Sheppey, "Pray have a care of my Syder, it costs me deare"- presumably referring to the attention the cider might need in storage and in transport to Flamsteed at Greenwich, as well as discouraging the curate from drinking too much of it!

Another season of the year when Flamsteed regularly visited

Burstow was at Christmas. At this special time of year, it must have been pleasant for he and his wife Margaret to leave the observatory at Greenwich for a week or two in the Surrey countryside, particularly as Margaret was from that area and no doubt had many friends and relatives there with whom to keep in touch. Travelling on the unmade roads at that time of the year would not have been too easy and John Flamsteed's health was always more of a problem in the winter, but this annual Christmas visit must have kept the Flamsteeds in contact with family and parish affairs at Burstow and would have been particularly enjoyed by Margaret.

Flamsteed, like all those engaged in a scientific career, could never really take a holiday and forget completely the work which occupied his mind. During his summer visit to Burstow he would take sufficient of his books and papers so that he could continue with his calculations, even if he did no observations. He would also take along some of his pupils so that they could continue their education and at the same time enjoy a change of air and scenery and doubtless in return he would endeavour to get them to help him with routine and simple mathematical calculations.

Following the dismissal of his High Church curate in 1715, Flamsteed set about improving the condition of his rectory - which stands adjacent to the church in Burstow. During his summertime visit in 1716 he was kept busy supervising the demolition of a large part of the rectory and organising its reconstruction. This project again demonstrates that Flamsteed was not lacking in energy, nor in planning for the future or looking after the affairs of the church, despite his being 70 years old at this time. The rebuilding work was completed in time for his visit the following Christmas and on December 28th, suitably regaled by Christmas fare and relaxing in a more comfortable rectory, he again wrote to Abraham Sharp, "I have rebuilt three-quarters of my parsonage house at Burstow, at about £120 charge, so that 'tis now the best in the country." The old rectory with the extensive addition made by order of John Flamsteed still stands adjoining the southern perimeter of the churchyard and can be reached from the church by descending a small flight of steps.

Sadly the Revd. John Flamsteed was not to occupy his renovated parsonage for many more years. He died on the last day of 1719 and his astronomer colleague, the Revd. James Pound, who had previously been chaplain to the British East India Company and Rector of Wanstead in Essex, succeeded Flamsteed in the living of Burstow.

The body of John Flamsteed and that of his wife Margaret lie beneath the chancel of Burstow Church, in front of the altar. Two plaques are positioned on nearby walls, one commemorating Flamsteed the Astronomer Royal and the other in commemoration of his long period of service as Rector of Burstow from 1684 to 1719. The vault of the Cooke family is situated behind the altar and there rests the body of Margaret Flamsteed's grandfather, the Revd. Ralph Cooke, DD, who was Rector of Burstow from 1637 to 1684. One senses that the Flamsteeds were held in honour and admiration by their parishioners in Burstow and that they would find respect and a haven of peace amongst the community there during their visits. This esteem for the Flamsteed name still lives on, perpetuated by the memorial east window of the church which illustrates "The Star in the East and the Visit of the Magi" at the nativity of Christ. This window was made for the 1975 tercentenary of Flamsteed's appointment as Astronomer Royal and in Burstow he is suitably remembered not only as a famous astronomer but as a conscientious former rector who served the parish for the long period of thirty five years.

Chapter XIII
Flamsteed's Work after 1712

Following the great disappointment which John Flamsteed felt after the publication in 1712 of Halley's edition of his work, there arose inside him a strong determination (probably fuelled by his anger) that he would persevere with and publish at his own expense, his own correct version of the star catalogue. For several years he had become increasingly aware that the scientific establishment, in the shape of Newton, Halley and other eminent Fellows of the Royal Society, as well as his royal sponsors, had drifted away from him and were largely unaware of the great work he was pursuing. There was unlikely to be any further help from such quarters and he now had to rely entirely upon his own resources. Fortunately, he had a wife who was equally dedicated to the task of seeing her husband's work appropriately recognised in a published form. Also James Hodgson, his former assistant who had married Flamsteed's niece Anna Heming and was now Mathematics Master at Christ's Hospital School in London, was a very capable astronomer who understood the work of the Royal Observatory and would undoubtedly help Flamsteed in any way he could. Hodgson, however, had to be careful not to align himself too closely with Flamsteed lest this should affect his position in the scientific community. Flamsteed valued Hodgson as one of the most capable of his former assistants and had been very sorry when Hodgson left the Royal Observatory in 1702. Now, more than ten years later, he began to feel a little unsure about Hodgson, and thought that he was not a very strong personality but one who might be swayed by pressure exerted upon him by those in authority. As a Fellow of the Royal Society and a close relative, however, James Hodgson was a useful ally to have as Flamsteed pressed on towards the goal of having a true edition of his work published.

The determination and confidence which John Flamsteed showed at this time of his life, when he was now 66 years old and increasingly affected by regular episodes of poor health (principally gout and intensely painful renal stones), is quite remarkable. One can speculate as to whether this was just part of his natural stubborn character or if he drew somehow on hidden resources which he derived from his belief in God. Certainly, he constantly referred in his writing to the dependence he placed on the goodness of God in allowing him to have made so much progress in his work and the confidence he had that he would be able to complete it. "God has conducted and blessed my work hitherto, and I will not doubt of his bringing it to perfection [completeness], and affording means to publish it, for the more manifesting the wisdom of his works and the good of an ingenious people, that loves truth both for its own sake and its usefulness."

In full confidence that his star catalogue would eventually be published, at the end of 1712 Flamsteed had his portrait drawn by the artist Thomas Gibson so that this could be used as the frontispiece of his first volume. Previously, Flamsteed had not been wealthy enough to go to the expense of such an undertaking and pictures of him are rare but now he saw his portrait as an integral part of the intended publication. He wrote that the artist "has done it very well and like. I purpose to have it engraved on copper for a half sheet, as large as those of my catalogue." A portrait of Flamsteed, almost identical to the engraving which forms the frontispiece to his star catalogue, is displayed in the Derby Museum and Art Gallery (see figure 14).

Figure 14.
John Flamsteed at the age of 66 years.
A similar engraving was to form the frontispiece in the
'Historia Coelestis Britannica', and the hand-on-heart posture
perhaps indicates that this contains true data as opposed to that
published in Halley's 'pirated' version.
By courtesy of the trustees of Derby Museum and Art Gallery.

Abraham Sharp, the former assistant at the observatory who had now retired to the village of Little Horton in Yorkshire, remained one of Flamsteed's closest friends and supporters. There was a great mutual respect between these two men and although they probably never again met, there was constant correspondence between them. Possibly Sharp did not share the confidence that Flamsteed expressed, that his life would be spared until the great work was completed (which included finishing a survey of all the northern constellations), for in August 1713 he urged Flamsteed to go ahead and publish such results as were checked and ready. By this time, in fact, the first sheets of the catalogue were already being printed little by little and some of the early sheets were sent up to Abraham Sharp for his own use and possibly for his friendly opinion and comments on the work. Flamsteed urged him to take great care of these pre-publication sheets, as he was the only person to have them and if at any time he was to become seriously ill he must seal them up and send them back to the Greenwich Observatory to prevent them falling into the wrong hands. James Hodgson was not given any copies of these papers as Flamsteed feared they might be wheedled out of him and perhaps printed under some other person's name.

At the same time as this, Flamsteed was also pursuing through the Lord Chamberlain (the Duke of Bolton) his claim for ownership of the "pirated" edition of his work, published under Halley's editorship in 1712. Eventually and perhaps surprisingly, the Court decided in Flamsteed's favour and the Referees were ordered in the early part of 1716 to return all unsold copies of this work to the Astronomer Royal at Greenwich. This decision must have shaken the eminent members of the publishing committee very considerably but there was no way they could overrule this judgement for it was made under the king's authority. With rather ill grace, they wrote to "My Lord" stating that the books were still with the printer and bookseller, Awnsham Churchill of Paternoster Row in London and that the late Queen Anne had desired that copies of this work of the Royal Observatory should be sent to prominent men and institutions both in Britain and on the continent. They protested that Sir Isaac Newton had spent a good deal of his own money on the publication of this book and would now be out of pocket because of the Court's decision, whereas Flamsteed had been paid a gratuity of £125 for his contribution to the work. They said that although "Mr. Flamsteed has given us a great deal of trouble," yet they had "begged of Her Majesty the remainder of the copies for him." Whatever the truth of the matter, by the end of March 1716, the 300 unsold copies had been delivered to Flamsteed and he soon committed them to a bonfire in Greenwich Park. In doing this, which could have been interpreted by some as an act of terrible vandalism, Flamsteed intended both the destruction of information which was in some part faulty and might therefore mislead those who referred to it and also the preservation of his own good name and reputation. Flamsteed saw this conflagration not as a tragic end to the publication of his life's work but as a great opportunity now to present the complete and accurate version of his own star catalogue to the world. He wrote, "I bless that good Providence, that never fails me, for its assisting me at last," and so he was encouraged to carry on checking and recalculating his data so that his work would be as perfect as he could possibly make it.

Flamsteed envisaged that his published work would be in three volumes. The first volume would be data derived from his sextant measurements up to 1689 and was substantially the same as the first volume of Halley's 1712 publication, made up of the 97 sheets which Flamsteed had previously confirmed as correct. For the second volume Flamsteed required the 175 sheets of data he had collected with the mural arc between 1689 and 1705 and which he had given as unchecked and confidential information to Sir Isaac Newton on 20th March, 1708. He wrote to Newton on April 23rd, 1716, asking for the return of his "night notes" made between November 1678 and February 1684, together with these 175 sheets of mural arc observations. He seems to have recovered some of his original data "after nine and a half years captivity" as he put it, but it is unlikely that he received everything from Newton after so long a period. Flamsteed therefore had to recover this information from his own papers and check it before he dare go ahead with his second volume. The third volume was to contain a comparison of Flamsteed's observations with the star catalogues of earlier astronomers, together with information on the precession of the equinoxes and various supplementary tables. Another task, which Flamsteed commenced in September 1716, was to write a preface to his intended publication. This preface was not merely a few introductory pages for the front of his first volume but was a complete history of the development of astronomical methods and measurements from ancient times to his own day, extending to well over 50 pages. This preface has recently been republished as an interesting book in its own right (see Bibliography).

The "Board of Visitors", which Queen Anne had appointed in December 1710, consisting of selected members of the Royal Society to oversee the work of the observatory, did not lose its authority following the death of the Queen in 1714, as Flamsteed may have hoped. King George I perpetuated the function of this committee, which was to include an annual inspection of the equipment at the observatory, to see to the maintenance of any piece of equipment as required or to purchase whatever else was deemed necessary. Also, the Visitors were authorised to demand an annual report from the Astronomer Royal which would detail the work undertaken during the year and be available within six months of the year's end.

Through the next few years, in gradually failing health but with an indomitable spirit, Flamsteed continued writing towards his objective of completing a comprehensive and very accurate catalogue of the stars. Also, he continued to make more observations of the sky whenever he could. He continued to be a practical astronomer right to the end. In September 1718 he wrote, "I am now 72 years of age and have entered my 73rd. I thank God I have my health well for my years: and I doubt not but he will continue it, that I may finish what I have under my hands."

Towards the end of November 1719 however, Flamsteed began to suffer serious deterioration in his health. His handwriting and his signature, which had hitherto been bold and plain, became more of a scrawl - perhaps due to a minor cerebral perfusion abnormality or stroke. He was unable to visit his parish at Burstow that year for his usual Christmas break but remained at the Greenwich observatory. Shortly after Christmas, Flamsteed became seriously ill and was unable to retain any food, constantly vomiting up everything that he was given. This was of great concern to his wife Margaret and also to his assistant at the observatory, Joseph Crosthwait. On the last day of 1719, in the evening of Thursday 31st December, Flamsteed called for Crosthwait to come to him. He wished to say something to his assistant but was unable to communicate with him. John Flamsteed died at about 9.38 p.m. that night.

Joseph Crosthwait must have been an invaluable source of strength to Mrs. Flamsteed at this sad time as the Flamsteeds had no children to give her support. Margaret Flamsteed made the necessary arrangements for her husband's body to be buried in the church at Burstow. Crosthwait wrote to his friend, Abraham Sharp, describing in some detail the death of his employer, whom he describes as "that great and good man". The esteem which Crosthwait felt for Flamsteed is well conveyed in the letter which he wrote on January 2nd, 1720, where he states, "I shall always lament the loss the public will have of so valuable a man." It seems to have been a custom of those times to send a funeral ring to the closest friends of the deceased person and Crosthwait enquires of Abraham Sharp how such a ring could be delivered to him at his remote northern home.

At this same time, Joseph Crosthwait was faced with great changes in his own life - for with the death of the Astronomer Royal his own position at the observatory was now at an end. However, he made a great and noble resolution concerning the satisfactory conclusion of the work on which his former employer had been engaged. He wrote, "The love, honour and esteem I have, and shall always have for his memory and everything that belongs to him, will not permit me to leave Greenwich or London before I hope the three volumes are finished." In that way, he signalled a rare loyalty to John Flamsteed and a commitment to see the star catalogue through to the final publication. The task which this entailed was no easy one, although the first volume was no problem as it had already been completed under Flamsteed's supervision. The second volume also was nearly ready when Flamsteed died and could be finished with some careful work and perseverance. But the third volume, with its great historical preface, could only be completed by competent astronomers who understood Flamsteed's methods and the papers he had left behind. The work was only finished due to Joseph Crosthwait's dedication to his friend and colleague, the late John Flamsteed and he used all his endeavours to see the job through.

CHAPTER XIV

Consequences at Greenwich following Flamsteed's Death

John Flamsteed had occupied the Royal Observatory at Greenwich for more than 43 years when he died and during his last few years there the work had fallen into a steady regular routine. Observations of the night sky continued to be made on every suitable occasion and during the daytime recalculation and checking of the large mass of data he had acquired was going on to bring it to a state of readiness for the printers. On his death, which followed quite a short period of illness, this routine was interrupted and the observatory was thrown into a state of turmoil. Margaret Flamsteed was distraught at the loss of her husband, to whom she had been utterly devoted. The objective they had worked towards over a long period - the publication of the world's best catalogue of the fixed stars - was yet unattained and the house which had been her home for more than 27 years since her marriage would now have to be vacated.

It was less than six weeks after Flamsteed's death that his successor was appointed. Edmond Halley was made the second Astronomer Royal on February 9th, 1720 and he lost no time in visiting the observatory and giving Margaret Flamsteed orders to quit the premises. According to Joseph Crosthwait, who was the astronomy assistant at the time, Halley gave Mrs. Flamsteed only a few days to remove herself and all her belongings from the building. The appointment of Halley, John Flamsteed's great enemy, must have come as a terrible blow to Margaret Flamsteed following the death of her husband. She faced summary eviction from the house and could expect little sympathy from the new tenant. Her great source of strength was Joseph Crosthwait and with his assistance, in the few days granted her, she removed not only the furniture and fittings from the house but also all the instruments that legally belonged to her husband. The two Great Clocks were removed from their alcove in the Octagon Room, the Sextant, made by order of Sir Jonas Moore, was taken away from the Sextant House and the Mural Arc made by Abraham Sharp was taken from its mounting place on the Meridian Wall. The Sidereal Clock, made by Thomas Tompion, was also carried away, together with all Flamsteed's telescopes and the collection of smaller quadrants and micrometers which he had accumulated from his early days in Derbyshire. All Flamsteed's books and papers, with the records of observations covering more than four decades, were bundled up and taken away.

When Halley entered the Royal Observatory to take up residence there on March 7th, 1720, he must have been aghast at the prospect which confronted him. What had been the world's foremost observatory for positional astronomy was now stripped of all its equipment and incapable of performing the simplest measurement.

The majority of Flamsteed's equipment was eventually sold to help pay for his posthumous publications and unfortunately little of it still exists today. However, the Sidereal Clock and the movement from one of the Great Clocks can still be seen at Greenwich Observatory, together with Flamsteed's Meridian Line at the place where he spent so many long night hours observing the stars in their courses across the heavens. The Octagon Room and the living rooms of Flamsteed House are also preserved in a style which is probably very similar to that which they had in the 17th Century. An authentic atmosphere is conjured up in this part of the old building, which was home to the Flamsteeds for so many years, so that it is well worth a visit - particularly if some of the historical background is borne in mind.

Following Halley's discomfiture at having found the observatory with no instruments, the Office of Ordnance demanded that Mrs. Flamsteed return the Sextant and the two Great Clocks immediately, under threat of being taken to court. They said they had grounds to believe that Sir Jonas Moore had donated these "to the House, not the person." Margaret Flamsteed resisted this demand, repeating what John Flamsteed had always declared on many different occasions during his life and had left in his written documentary records - that all the equipment at the observatory was his own personal property. Abraham Sharp was prepared to support her by his testimony that the clocks and sextant were definitely gifts to Flamsteed from Sir Jonas Moore rather than instruments which belonged to the government. He had, of course, constructed the Mural Arc with his own hands and had received payment for this work directly from John Flamsteed. No one knew as much about the history of the instruments at the observatory as Abraham Sharp but Mrs. Flamsteed and Joseph Crosthwait still anticipated a difficult time with the Crown solicitors over proving their ownership of this equipment. The Office of Ordnance took counsel from the Attorney-General regarding the question of ownership and the decision seemed to hinge upon who had maintained or repaired the equipment. Although the Board of Visitors had commented on the condition of some of the instruments there was no evidence that they had ever actually repaired any of them, whereas Flamsteed had been responsible for their proper working order ever since he had taken the post of Astronomer Royal - at first using what was certainly his own equipment, which he had brought down from Derbyshire. By the end of 1720, the claims of the Office of Ordnance had become somewhat muted and they were considering the possible purchase of the sextant from Mrs. Flamsteed for Dr. Halley's use. In accordance with what would have been her late husband's wishes, she declined any suggestion of such a sale. Gradually the threat of legal action receded and by June 1721 the Board of Visitors and the Office of Ordnance gave up the claim they had made for possession of the equipment and took the decision not to proceed with their lawsuit against Mrs. Flamsteed.

Joseph Crosthwait, after notifying Abraham Sharp of Flamsteed's death, continued to correspond with him. Both men had much in common, having worked as assistants to Flamsteed and both had an intimate knowledge of the work of the observatory. In a letter to Sharp, written in May 1720, Crosthwait wryly comments on remarks made by Halley some years earlier. He remembers how Halley had always said that no one over the age of 60 should be Astronomer Royal but now he himself had accepted the office at the age of 64 years! In fact, Halley remained in occupation at the observatory until his death at the great age of 86 years.

For some time before Flamsteed died, Abraham Sharp had been helping him by checking and commenting upon printed sheets for the catalogue which had been regularly sent to him. Joseph Crosthwait now wrote to him, hoping that he will continue to assist in this way but the sudden manner in which they had been forced to vacate the observatory had "occasioned such confusion amongst Mr. Flamsteed's papers that I could not find a perfect copy of the last impression of his catalogue, which I presume, you have not yet seen." Also they had lost the working space provided by the rooms at the observatory, so the task of assembling the information into proper order for the catalogue would not be easy.

Halley was desperately short of equipment when he first moved in to the observatory. He faced the same situation as that which had met Flamsteed at the time of his appointment as Astronomer Royal in 1675 but Halley did not appear to have any equipment of his own (as Flamsteed had), nor did he have a generous sponsor like Sir Jonas Moore. Crosthwait heard that Halley had been forced to borrow a quadrant from the Royal Society so that he might start some observations but this instrument had proved to be of such poor quality that any sightings taken with it were virtually useless. The two former assistants at the observatory, who could work to the high standard of accuracy demanded by their former employer in all his work, were no doubt rather amused at the plight of the famous new Astronomer Royal. Eventually, Halley approached Joseph Crosthwait with the suggestion that he might return to the observatory to work for him but Crosthwait politely declined this offer. Although their paths in Greenwich must often have coincided, Crosthwait remained entirely aloof from Halley out of regard for his former employer's feelings.

Halley must have been mightily relieved when the Board of

Ordnance allocated him the sum of £500 for re-equipping the observatory but it was only in October 1721, more than 18 months after his arrival, that he was able to record any reliable observations. This allocation of government money for the instruments at the Greenwich Observatory set a new precedent and thereafter the equipment of the Royal Observatory was clearly the property of the government rather than of the Astronomer Royal who occupied the building and it was repaired and serviced out of government funds. At the end of 1721, Halley abandoned the Sextant and Quadrant House where Flamsteed had made most of his observations, converting this into a house for pigeons! This was not so much to eradicate all signs of Flamsteed's presence and to make a completely new start but rather in recognition of the fact that the meridian wall on which the Mural Arc had been mounted was slowly subsiding down the slope of the Greenwich hill - a fact of which Flamsteed had been aware and for which he had made corrections in his calculations. With the money allocated to him for instruments, Halley ordered a new 8-foot quadrant to be made together with a new clock for the Octagon Room from George Graham, who had been elected a Fellow of the Royal Society in 1721. Graham had married one of Thomas Tompion's nieces and had succeeded him in his clockmaking business, becoming Britain's foremost scientific instrument maker.

Halley eventually commenced a cycle of observations of the Moon which would last for 18 years and 11 days - the so-called Saros Cycle - after which the relative positions of the Sun and Moon recur. By accurately observing the Moon's position in the sky against the background of the fixed stars to within a few seconds of arc during this cycle, he hoped he might be able to predict its future course and perhaps win for himself the £20,000 longitude prize which had been offered in 1714 by the Board of Longitude. Halley realised that Sir Isaac Newton's calculations, which were based on Flamsteed's observations and the theory of gravity, had so far failed to solve this problem but continuous observations of the Moon over the long period of a Saros cycle might be more successful. Although he was 64 years of age when he became Astronomer Royal, he completed this long-term task but it was left for European mathematicians such as Euler,

D'Alembert, Clairaut, Mayer and others to gradually work towards a successful "theory of the Moon". Tobias Mayer's book *Nouvelles Tables de la Lune*, published in 1753, contained the first set of lunar tables calculated from gravitational principles which stood up to accurate observation. This work was shown to be sufficiently accurate for use in navigation by Nevil Maskelyne (Astronomer Royal from 1765 to 1811) during a voyage to and from St. Helena in 1761. Encouraged by this success in astronomical navigation, Maskelyne went on to publish the *British Mariner's Guide* in 1763 and the *Nautical Almanac* in 1766. This latter publication, of course, continues to be printed even to the present day. It was, therefore, about 90 years after King Charles II had appointed John Flamsteed as Astronomer Royal, to perfect the art of navigation through observations of the heavens, that navigation based on astronomical sightings became a practical possibility.

CHAPTER XV

Flamsteed's Historia Coelestis Britannica (1725) and Atlas Coelestis (1729)

O
ut of a sense of loyalty to his former employer and colleague, Joseph Crosthwait had vowed that he would not leave Greenwich or London until all three volumes of Flamsteed's work were in print but he realised that this would be no easy undertaking. Not only had the second and third volumes to be checked and completed in a way which would do honour to Flamsteed's reputation but also the financing of the requisite printing and drawing work had to be considered. It was time for Joseph Crosthwait to gather together his resources and weigh up the costs involved. Fortunately, he had worked with John Flamsteed for some years and fully understood his observing techniques and his methods of calculation. Mrs. Flamsteed was a capable and shrewd woman who would have to bear the expenses of printing and engraving, but she was devoted to her husband and keenly desired to see his work concluded in an appropriate manner. Joseph Crosthwait was not a wealthy person and his salary as the observatory assistant must have been quite small, so the finance had to come through Mrs. Flamsteed.

John Flamsteed had made a will which outlined his possessions and nominated his wife Margaret and his niece, Mrs. James Hodgson, as executrixes. He stipulated that two coats should be given to impoverished men of the parish of Burstow, under the beneficence of his wife. In cash terms he left only around £350 as capital that was readily available. He had, however, made provision for the sum of £120 per year to be paid to his wife, together with another £50 per year which was hers by right - as it probably came from her family or from the sale of property belonging to her family in London. This gave Mrs. Flamsteed an income of £170 per year. However, some of her money was invested in South Sea Stock and may have been lost with the catastrophic bursting of the "South Sea Bubble" in 1720. After her death, all remaining assets were to be equally divided between Flamsteed's kinsman and namesake, John Flamsteed, who lived at Little Hallam in Derbyshire (who had probably been a pupil of Flamsteed at the observatory in 1692) and Mrs. Hodgson's children. These limited financial resources would have to be carefully employed if they were to cover the costs involved in publishing the three intended volumes.

Joseph Crosthwait's greatest asset was Abraham Sharp - that elderly man now living in retirement at Little Horton in Yorkshire - who, in his younger days, had been recognised by Flamsteed as "an excellent geometrician and mathematician" and had constructed the Mural Arc which had been such a wonderful instrument in Flamsteed's hands from 1689. Although Sharp was now nearing 70 years of age he still retained his mathematical skills and was still a good draughtsman - a talent which he had cultivated in Flamsteed's company, when he had become an expert in graduating the fine circumferential scales necessary for astronomical quadrants. Abraham Sharp also retained his interest in astronomy and seeing he was now retired he had the time to devote to the task which now presented itself. Without his help it is very doubtful if Joseph Crosthwait could have fulfilled his promise of seeing the three volumes finished.

James Hodgson, although living in London and being the nearest relative of the Flamsteeds, seems to have made little contribution to the task of publishing the star catalogue. Despite his coming into possession of the huge mass of papers which Flamsteed left behind, he seems to have shown little interest in getting any of it published. When Lunar Tables, identical to those left unpublished by Flamsteed, were published by the Frenchman Le Monnier in his book *Institutions Astronomique* of 1746, Hodgson was astonished, declaring that he had intended to get these tables of John Flamsteed published sometime and was puzzled as to how they had fallen into foreign hands. These tables of the Moon's positions were obviously still important enough for general publication even 26 years after Flamsteed's death. This slow-moving characteristic of James Hodgson bears out what Flamsteed had said about him much earlier - "He is of a very mild and easy temper." Joseph Crosthwait was not long in making up his mind concerning the contribution which Hodgson might make towards the publishing of Flamsteed's works - "We can depend but very little upon Mr. Hodgson," he wrote to Abraham Sharp in May, 1720.

As we have mentioned earlier, Hodgson may have been reluctant to associate himself too closely with Flamsteed because of his position as Mathematics Master at Christ's Hospital and not wanting to make himself unpopular with friends of Sir Isaac Newton or Edmond Halley. Both these men were in high positions and had influence in the Royal Society, in Government and in the Universities, so it would be unwise from a career point of view to fall foul of such men. Whatever support Hodgson was to provide would be done quietly and behind the scenes.

Once the threat of legal action over the possession of Flamsteed's instruments was out of the way, (for this could have completely wrecked their limited finances), the little "Flamsteed Team" forged ahead with its plans for publishing John Flamsteed's work. Joseph Crosthwait was the co-ordinator and power-house in London, whilst Abraham Sharp, in the seclusion of his house at Little Horton in Yorkshire, was the skilled calculator and draughtsman. Mrs. Flamsteed kept tight control of the purse-strings and allocated only a little money to the printers as and when this was necessary. The co-operation between Crosthwait and Sharp was outstanding - they were true friends and colleagues and Crosthwait kept Sharp fully informed of developments in London when he issued and received back the sheets which would be printed as the final catalogue of the stars. Both men knew that the final publication would be scrutinised by the critical eye of Edmond Halley and so they did all in their power to avoid mistakes that he might seize on to diminish the public acclaim which they hoped the catalogue would receive.

Through Joseph Crosthwait, Mrs. Flamsteed requested Abraham Sharp to undertake the remaining artistic and geometrical work, promising to reimburse him for his labour - a promise which it is very doubtful she ever kept. In August 1720, she herself wrote to Sharp to thank him for the great assistance he was giving and in particular for drawing the outlines of a further six constellations. She describes herself as still being "under the greatest grief possible for the death of Mr. Flamsteed, which made me incapable of almost everything." She was living in Greenwich at this time but at some distance from the observatory. Without the help of Crosthwait and Sharp she would have been at a loss to know how to proceed with her husband's work. A later comment from the Dutch engraver, Van der Gucht, stated that "he had never seen any figures so well performed in all his life" as those of Abraham Sharp on the margins of the star maps, so we must conclude that Sharp's work was of a very high quality.

The Flamsteed team also requested the eminent artist, Sir James Thornhill, who had been employed by both Queen Anne and King George I, to assist with the work of drawing star maps, received in outline from Abraham Sharp and to prepare them for the engraver. Sir James had painted eight scenes inside the dome of St. Paul's Cathedral and also the walls and ceiling of the Painted Hall at the Royal Hospital, Greenwich, (which later became the Royal Naval College). On this ceiling, John Flamsteed and his assistant Thomas Weston are shown with the Mural Arc in a picture which also illustrates the prediction of a total solar eclipse for 9.03 a.m. on April 22nd, 1715. (This prediction was correct; the date relates to the Old Style Julian calendar which was used in Britain until 1752 and would be reckoned on our modern Gregorian calendar as May 3rd, 1715). The publishing team were fortunate in securing the services of such a well-known artist who would add his reputation to the final production, but it seems that after difficulties were encountered with the engraving work Sir James Thornhill lost interest in further work on the star maps. He suggested the Dutchman, Van der Gucht, as a possible engraver and for some time he was employed on the work. However, after the completion of plates for the constellations Taurus and Leo, Van der Gucht began to ask rather exorbitant fees for his work.

Crosthwait complained to Sir James Thornhill that the Dutchman he had recommended was becoming far too expensive. Sir James agreed that 10 guineas per map should be quite adequate for the work (he himself received only £3 per square yard for the ceiling and only £1 for the walls of the Painted Hall) but after some disagreement with Van der Gucht Mrs. Flamsteed paid him 25 guineas for the two plates.

Getting the star maps suitably engraved became a continual headache for Joseph Crosthwait. He was held down to a very low budget by Mrs. Flamsteed, whilst on the other hand every competent engraver was charging high fees. One engraver, a Mr. Nutting, had sold plates entrusted to him and disappeared, which was a huge blow to Joseph Crosthwait. He wrote to Abraham Sharp saying that he was almost at his wits' end and "I can justly say, of all the trouble I have met with since Mr. Flamsteed's death, none has come up to this…What to do I know not."

Crosthwait had already sent some of the maps to Holland, hoping to find an engraver there who would work satisfactorily for smaller fees. Now he decided to travel to Holland himself, to see if personal contact with Dutch engravers might provide a cheaper means of getting the job done. He set sail for Rotterdam on Wednesday, April 16th, 1722 and after a difficult and dangerous crossing of the North Sea, he arrived there four days later. He searched throughout the area for over a week without finding a suitable engraver and then decided to travel on to Amsterdam, reaching there on April 29th. Here he spent two weeks, in some difficulty because he was unable to speak the language and therefore at a disadvantage when bargaining with Dutch craftsmen. At last, he had a stroke of luck, when he chanced to meet a friendly merchant who knew the Flamsteeds, having supplied John Flamsteed with all his paper and from whom Mrs. Flamsteed had purchased the paper for the star catalogue. The Dutch merchant helped Crosthwait find an engraver who would only charge £6.16.3d for each plate. Also he agreed to act as the intermediary through whom this payment could be made, so that Mrs. Flamsteed would deal directly with him, relieving Joseph Crosthwait of any involvement in transferring money to Holland.

Crosthwait felt satisfied that his visit to Holland had been successful and he now attempted to book his passage back home but he found this was no easy matter. Having made his way back to Rotterdam, he was unable to find any boat sailing to London for a period of five weeks - time which he could have used much more profitably at home. Eventually, the same yacht on which he had crossed the North Sea some two months earlier came into port. Crosthwait knew the steward of this boat and despite the hazardous crossing they had experienced before, he bravely took passage on the yacht. The steward (perhaps conscious of the rough passage his friend had previously made) gave him a free ticket for the voyage, thus saving the fare of £5. Crosthwait thought that Mrs. Flamsteed should have paid him for the time and trouble he had spent on this visit to Holland, which had been quite demanding on him but he told Abraham Sharp in his next letter that he had received nothing from her as yet. Neither did he expect anything, as he had no written agreement over his expenses and he doubted that Sharp would receive anything either. Both these men were of a noble spirit and expended themselves entirely out of the admiration and respect they had for their former employer.

It might have been supposed that the preface, already written by John Flamsteed in English, could easily have been translated into Latin for publication but here again there was considerable difficulty. At first the Revd. James Pound, who had succeeded Flamsteed as Rector of Burstow and who had known John Flamsteed for many years, was asked to undertake the translation. As a clergyman he was expected to have a good standard of written Latin and as he had been a practising astronomer for many years it was assumed he would be familiar with the history of astronomy that Flamsteed had described. However, by July 1722, he had made practically no progress with the translation, pleading lack of time. Crosthwait became suspicious that either Edmond Halley or Sir Isaac Newton was discouraging him from proceeding with the work. That October, Mrs. Flamsteed sent a special messenger to discuss the matter with James Pound and because he had made no further progress the Flamsteed manuscript and the books which had been lent to him to help in his task were brought back to her.

The next person asked to translate the manuscript was a colleague of James Hodgson at Christ's Hospital - a schoolmaster who was thought to be proficient in Latin. But when the first part of his translation was shown to William Whiston (the former Lucasian Professor of Mathematics at Cambridge) and to Dr. James Jurin they concluded that Flamsteed's meaning had been misunderstood in some instances and they were rather unhappy with the standard of Latin that had been written. The printing of the preface was therefore held up whilst some more competent translator could be found. Mrs. Flamsteed and James Hodgson were willing to pay 10 shillings per printed sheet for a good translation, which seems quite generous in view of the fact that a university professor at that time might only be paid £100 per year. Finally a relative of Margaret Flamsteed suggested that the Revd. Anderson, a Presbyterian minister living in St. James', London, might prove suitable. Crosthwait sent a copy of one sheet of Flamsteed's manuscript to him as a preliminary test and was immensely relieved when William Whiston declared the result to be excellent Latin. The translation proceeded forthwith, albeit at much greater expense than had been anticipated as the Revd. Anderson demanded one guinea per page for the first ten pages and £2 per sheet thereafter.

Some bitter comments made by John Flamsteed about the conduct of Halley and Newton in respect of the 1712 version of his works were deleted from his manuscript before it was printed. It was probably thought that criticism of these well-respected men could damage sales of the books as well as harm the future careers of those involved in the publication - James Hodgson and Joseph Crosthwait in particular.

Eventually, the work of checking the data for the star catalogue was finished, the Latin translation of the preface was completed and the printer had all the material necessary for all three volumes which Flamsteed had envisaged. Joseph Crosthwait must have been heartily relieved that this duty, which he had vowed to fulfil, was nearly over. In a letter to Abraham Sharp, dated April 17th, 1725, he wrote, "I can now assure you that, God Willing, nothing can hinder everything from being printed by the 30th of this instant." The printer did not work quite as rapidly as Crosthwait had anticipated and it was the middle of June before all the books were delivered from the printer's workshop. The work, entitled

Historia Coelestis Britannica (British History of the Heavens) of 1725, was dedicated to King George I in the names of Margaret Flamsteed and James Hodgson. Joseph Crosthwait's first task on receiving the books was to select one of each volume and despatch these in a parcel to Abraham Sharp by the Bradford carrier. It was a small, though no doubt warmly received reward for the invaluable contribution which Sharp had made to this remarkable publication.

The three volumes of *Historia Coelestis Britannica* were sold for eight guineas per set and the booksellers were given one extra set of books for every six that they sold. In modern values, the set of books, which in 1725 cost eight guineas, would today cost something of the order of one thousand pounds. Later, it seems, the price had to be reduced to five guineas because the Dutch threatened to print copies on the continent of Europe unless they were supplied at a cheaper rate. There was no international copyright protection in those days.

In 1726 Margaret Flamsteed, via the Lord Bishop of Chester, presented the three corrected volumes of *Historia Coelestis Britannica* to the Bodleian Library in Oxford. They remain in that library to the present day.

The arduous task of seeing Flamsteed's star catalogue through to completion and its final publication brought out the best in his former colleagues, Abraham Sharp and Joseph Crosthwait. They had formed the active nucleus of the Flamsteed team, without which the work would never have been done. They collaborated in a thoroughly professional manner, with a friendly spirit which must have lightened their task. In a most agreeable gesture, Abraham Sharp, who had retained his skill as an instrument maker, constructed a small quadrant as a present for Crosthwait that must have been highly valued by its recipient. Crosthwait, on his part, sent Sharp an historical book written by Bishop Gilbert Burnet which had belonged to John Flamsteed and would therefore make a fitting souvenir of their former director.

In the autumn of 1725, again with no anticipation of being paid for the vital role he would have to play in the work it entailed, Joseph Crosthwait urged Mrs. Flamsteed to proceed with the publication of a star atlas which would form a suitable reference and accessory to the catalogue. Such an atlas had been planned by Flamsteed as part of his three volumes, but, at the end of 1724, James Hodgson had called a halt to the engraving of any more star maps - presumably because of the high cost of the project and their limited financial resources. Now, with the prospect of money coming in from the sale of the star catalogue, Crosthwait thought that the atlas should be completed as a fitting embellishment to the three volumes of Flamsteed's observational data. He reminded Mrs. Flamsteed that Abraham Sharp had already drawn diagrams for many of the constellations and also the complete northern and southern hemispheres, out of respect for herself and John Flamsteed and it would make poor sense to cast away this valuable work. Also he hinted that if nothing was done with the charts which already existed, Abraham Sharp might print them himself for his own profit. Mrs. Flamsteed was thus persuaded to persevere with the star maps and the drawing of the northern hemisphere was sent for engraving to a young English engraver who had recently completed his apprenticeship and was seeking work. This man worked from premises situated near Tower Hill in London and was therefore conveniently near at hand and able to offer a considerably less expensive service than were the Dutch craftsmen. Abraham Sharp was once more called upon to give assistance and his unique abilities as mathematician and accurate draughtsman ensured that the stars were correctly represented geometrically on the plates.

Crosthwait encountered similar difficulties with the engraver to those he had experienced before and the work proceeded so slowly that he began negotiations again with the Dutch artist, Van der Gucht, despite the exorbitant fees he had charged for his earlier work. None of the engravers seemed to be keen to produce star maps - probably because the work required very accurate geometry as well as their usual degree of artistic skill. Eventually, however, the work was finished and Joseph Crosthwait's ambition to see all the work of John Flamsteed put into print and backed up by a volume of star maps was fulfilled. The *Atlas Coelestis* was published in 1729, nearly ten years after the death of the first Astronomer Royal who had so painstakingly observed the stars and accurately plotted the positions of around 3,000 of them over a period of 44 years. The Star Atlas was dedicated to King George II - the first Hanoverian King, George I, having died in 1727 - and it was greeted with more praise and less controversy than Flamsteed's *Historia Coelestis Britannica* of 1725. Sir Isaac Newton had died in March 1727 and Edmond Halley was now busily engaged in a series of measurements on the position of the Moon which he hoped might win him the £20,000 Longitude Prize.

It was not long after this, on the 29th of July, 1730, that Mrs. Margaret Flamsteed died and was buried alongside her husband in the church at Burstow in Surrey. At least she had lived long enough to see his life's work completed in the published volumes of *Historia Coelestis Britannica* and the *Atlas Coelestis*. In her will she left nothing to Joseph Crosthwait or Abraham Sharp, which was rather negligent towards these men who had gone to so much trouble in order to see her late husband's work suitably recorded for posterity. Crosthwait wrote to Abraham Sharp, informing him of Mrs. Flamsteed's death and saying that he could not understand why she had made no recognition of their services. He himself had made great financial sacrifices in order to assist her, having turned down the offer of employment at the Royal Observatory made by Edmond Halley and had also refused an offer of a post at the Office of Ordnance, which carried a salary of £80 per year, at the behest of Mrs. Flamsteed. It seems a great pity that this apparent ingratitude of Margaret Flamsteed should have ended the association of the Flamsteed team, which had worked effectively for ten years, on such a sour note.

However, the Flamsteed books were now on sale - a lasting testimonial to a lifetime spent in "rectifying the tables of motion of the heavens and the places of the fixed stars," as King Charles had commanded so long before. There is no doubt that John Flamsteed would have been greatly pleased by the efforts of his former colleagues and proud of the star catalogue and atlas that had been published in his name. These reference volumes contained the best data on the positions of the heavenly bodies available for the next hundred years and have been termed "the astronomical bedrock of the 18th Century." They placed Britain at the forefront of astronomy throughout the world and were influential in all European countries, being printed in French until at least 1795 and forming part of Francis Baily's *Account of the Reverend John Flamsteed,* published in 1835.

The Flamsteed works have been described as "the proudest production of the Royal Observatory at Greenwich" and it has been said that in practical, observational astronomy they match the level of the theoretical studies which Sir Isaac Newton achieved in his *Principia*. If this is true, then John Flamsteed can have few rivals amongst 17th Century astronomers and his name, together with those of his two faithful assistants, Joseph Crosthwait and Abraham Sharp, must always command our utmost respect.

Appendix I

Some Astronomical Instruments of Flamsteed's Time

A. The Simple Quadrant. (See figure 15)

As the name indicates, this instrument comprised a quarter of a circle, carefully graduated on its circumference with a scale of degrees and parts of degrees and pivoted at its centre. The extreme radius carried sighting rings which could be aligned with a star or planet to determine its angle from the zenith (i.e.vertically overhead) by means of the plumb-line which was suspended from the central point. Obviously the greater the radius of the quadrant the more finely could the periphery be graduated and thus the more accurately could angles be read off the scale.

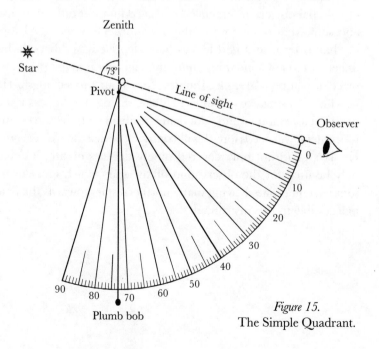

Figure 15.
The Simple Quadrant.

B. Robert Hooke's Mural Quadrant of 10ft Radius. (1676) (See figures 16 and 17)

John Flamsteed requested that a Mural Quadrant be provided at the Greenwich Observatory when it opened in 1676, so that he might measure the angles of stars from the zenith (vertically overhead) as they crossed the north-south meridian and also establish the Sun's position. Because the money which Sir Jonas Moore was willing to provide was inadequate to build such an instrument to Flamsteed's own design, Robert Hooke offered to design and construct a Quadrant of 10 ft radius quite cheaply. A brick wall, which ran accurately north-south was built by Flamsteed on which to fix the frame of the quadrant and a radial arm (or alidade) carried a telescopic sight which could be adjusted by means of a tangent-screw mechanism which engaged with teeth on the periphery of the quadrant. This screw mechanism required 17.88 turns of the handle to move the sight through an angle of one degree and carried a calibrated circular dial which enabled seconds of arc to be read off. Although it was conceived in theory to offer a very useful and accurate means of measuring the angles of celestial objects, in practice Flamsteed found it difficult to use and somewhat dangerous to the operators. He wrote, "...I tore my hands by it and had like to have deprived Cuthbert of his fingers... Except something more manageable may be put in its place, it will be a great let [hindrance] to our proceedings". He was rather dismissive of Robert Hooke, saying that he was not a practical astronomer and "not being troubled with the use of any instrument, will needs force his ill-contrived devices on us." Because Hooke's quadrant only covered ninety degrees of arc, it could only be used for the observation of the stars which crossed the southern meridian, leaving many northern stars towards the pole inaccessible to this instrument.

Figure 16.
Robert Hooke's 10ft Radius Mural Quadrant.
By courtesey of the National Maritime Museum, London

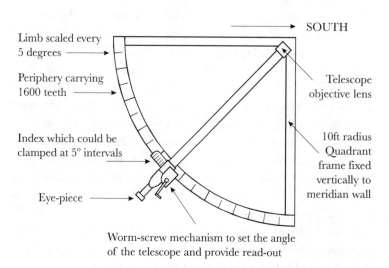

Figure 17.
Explanatory diagram of Robert Hooke's 10ft Radius Mural Quadrant.

C. Flamsteed's 7ft Radius Sextant. (1676)
(See figures 18 and 19)

A Sextant comprises one sixth of a full circle. This instrument enabled Flamsteed to determine the angle between any two heavenly bodies up to 60 degrees apart. It had a radius of 6 ft 9.25 inches from the centre to the outer edge of the circular arc. It was constructed by the craftsmen at the Tower of London under the orders of Sir Jonas Moore. The design was based on earlier sextants used by Tycho Brahe and Johannes Hevelius but was improved by Flamsteed to work with telescopic sights (giving the possibility of much greater accuracy). It had gear teeth on its periphery cut at the rate of 17 teeth per inch, which engaged with a graduated worm-screw mechanism similar to that of Hooke's quadrant.

The plane of the sextant could be adjusted into the plane of the two objects to be observed by means of two independent screw mechanisms operating on two toothed semicircles. The whole instrument was fixed on an equatorial mount, another Flamsteed innovation, facilitating the tracking of stars as the Earth rotates on its axis.

One observer manned the fixed telescope, keeping the first star centred on the cross-wires, whilst the second adjusted the moveable telescope using the screw mechanism to sight the second star. A third assistant kept the sextant in the correct observational plane and was needed if the clock had to be read or figures written down in the "night-notes". The screw mechanism was calibrated so that the angle between the two telescopes could be obtained firstly by knowing the number of screw turns between the stars and secondly (because Flamsteed found that the screw mechanism was quickly affected by wear of the teeth on the outer limb) by a conventionally graduated scale on the limb. Flamsteed found that it was very useful to cross-check the readings given by each of these calibration facilities.

Flamsteed's sextant worked very well and was used for his most important observations from September 1676 to September 1689, when it was effectively superseded by the Mural Arc.

Figure 18.
Etching by Francis Place of Flamsteed's 7ft Equatorially Mounted
Sextant (Anterior and Posterior views).
By courtesy of the National Maritime Museum, London.

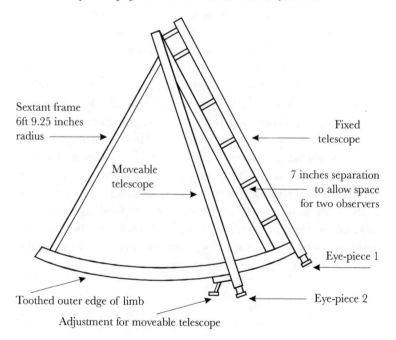

Sextant frame
6ft 9.25 inches
radius

Fixed
telescope

Moveable
telescope

7 inches separation
to allow space
for two observers

Eye-piece 1

Toothed outer edge of limb

Eye-piece 2

Adjustment for moveable telescope

Figure 19.
Diagram illustrating Flamsteed's 7ft Equatorially Mounted Sextant.

D. Flamsteed's 7ft Radius Mural Arc. (1689)
(See figures 20 and 21)

This instrument is illustrated in the third volume of *Historia Coelestis Britannica* of 1725, where it is entitled "Arcus Meridionalis" because it was fixed on the meridional west wall of the Quadrant House which was built to run accurately north-south. This diagram, however, does not show the worm-gear or screw mechanism at the observer's end of the telescope alidade which enabled the angle of the telescopic sight to be read off. This mechanism was probably very similar to that used with Flamsteed's sextant. A distinct advantage of this instrument over Hooke's quadrant was that the telescope could be moved through an angle of about 140 degrees in the plane of the arc (the meridian or north-south plane) and the altitude of any star visible from Greenwich could be measured using this instrument. The scale was calibrated by careful observation of a bright star which was vertically overhead in the Draco constellation.

The Mural Arc was constructed, calibrated and engraved by Abraham Sharp. It took 14 months to build and cost Flamsteed over £120. Flamsteed wrote that Sharp "contrived each part of it so ingeniously that his work was admired by all the expert craftsmen who beheld it...they acknowledged that they themselves could not have executed it with greater precision." The instrument was first used in September 1689 and it became Flamsteed's chief observing device for the next thirty years. He was highly delighted with its performance, commenting, "I found that whatever I sought with the sextant might, with less labor and more accuracy, be obtained with this instrument and the clock alone." The vertical angle of a star (known to astronomers as the Declination) would be obtained from the reading of the Mural Arc and the east-west position (known as the Right Ascension) by the time shown on the pendulum clock kept in the observing house.

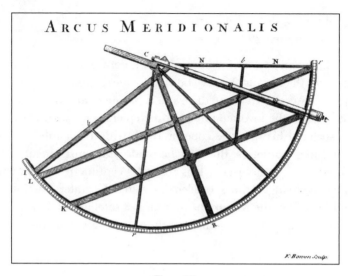

Figure 20.
Flamsteed's Mural Arc, built by Abraham Sharp in 1689.
By courtesy of the National Maritime Museum.

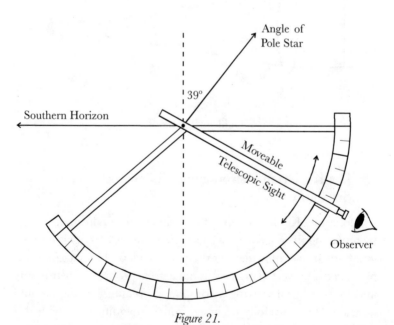

Figure 21.
This diagram illustrates how the angle of any star, including the Pole
Star, could be sighted and measured with this device.

E. The Galilean Telescope.
(See figure 22)

This early type of telescope uses a convex lens as objective (towards the distant object to be viewed) and a concave lens as the eye-piece as shown in the diagram. It produces an upright image rather than the inverted image of a Keplerian telescope. Galileo constructed his first telescope in 1609, with a magnification of only three diameters. But later he made other instruments - his largest having an objective lens about 4.4 centimetres in diameter and magnifying 33 times. Galileo discovered the craters, mountains and "seas" on the Moon, the four largest satellites of Jupiter, the phases of the planet Venus and the starry nature of the Milky Way.

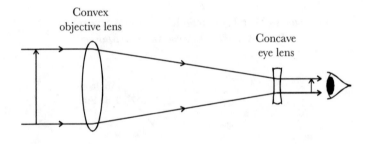

Figure 22.
Galilean Telescope

F. The Keplerian (Astronomical) Telescope.
(See figure 23)

Johannes Kepler modified the design of the Galilean telescope by replacing the concave eye lens with a convex lens. This had the great advantage of widening the field of view. The fact that this produced an inverted image was not a great problem in astronomy and for terrestrial viewing a compound erecting eye-piece could be used. With carefully designed optics, magnification with this type of telescope can extend up to 1,000 times. Keplerian telescopes are, because of their basic design, longer than Galilean telescopes and some in the 17th Century exceeded 200 feet in length, being suspended from tall poles (like that shown on the engravings of the Royal Observatory - figures 4 and 7, pages 38 and 47) or attached to tall towers. Objective lenses of very long focal length tended to reduce the image defect known as chromatic aberration, as well as making higher magnification possible. A further advantage of the Keplerian design was that cross-wires or a calibrated graticule (or a micrometer such as Flamsteed used) could be placed in the focal plane of the lenses, making the telescope more accurate as a sighting device and the precise measurement of small angles between two objects possible.

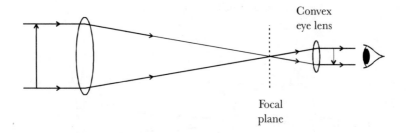

Convex
eye lens

Focal
plane

Figure 23.
Keplerian Telescope

G. The Gregorian Reflector Telescope.
(See figure24)

The Scottish mathematician James Gregory, who corresponded with Flamsteed, suggested the design of a reflector telescope which employed a mirror instead of an objective lens in his *Optica Promota* of 1663. He was not a skilled practical craftsman, however, and neither he nor the opticians he knew were able to produce a satisfactory mirror - particularly as in this design the main mirror required a hole at its centre to allow the image to be viewed by means of a suitable eye-piece. The Frenchman, N. Cassegrain, who was professor at Chartres College near Paris, produced a similar design (figure 25) which involved a secondary convex mirror and presented this to the Academie des Sciences in 1672. However, neither Gregory nor Cassegrain was able to make a working reflector telescope and it was about one hundred years before telescopes were routinely made to the Gregorian design.

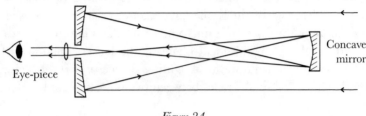

Figure 24.
Gregorian Telescope Design.

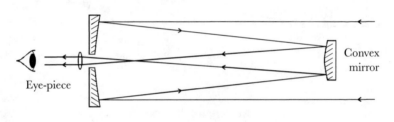

Figure 25.
Cassegrain Telescope Design.

H. The Newtonian Reflector Telescope.
   (See figure 26)

Because of colour defects in the image produced by any telescope which employs lenses (due to chromatic aberration), Sir Isaac Newton, in 1668, designed and constructed the first successful reflector telescope. This used a concave mirror to form the primary image and a small plane mirror which deflected the light to the side of the telescope to where the eye-piece was situated. Newton ground and polished the mirror, which had a concave spherical form, from a special alloy of copper and tin known as speculum -

metal. He presented his second telescope to the Royal Society on January 11th, 1672. This had a magnification of 38 times and employed a mirror of about 5 centimetres diameter and 16 centimetres focal length. Reflector telescopes, because of their basic design, are generally shorter than a refractor of similar magnifying power.

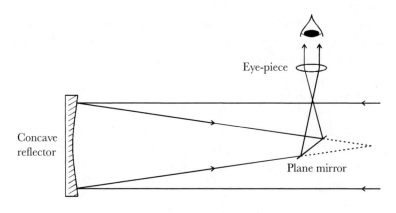

Figure 26.
Newton's Reflector Telescope.

I. Flamsteed's Sidereal Clock (1691).
(See figures 27 and 28)

This long-case clock, made for John Flamsteed, in 1691, by the master instrument maker Thomas Tompion, stands today very near the spot from which Flamsteed performed the majority of his observations using the Mural Arc and which is termed "Flamsteed's Meridian". The visitor to the Old Greenwich Observatory may be puzzled by the dial of this clock (see illustrations), which has the outer periphery divided into ten parts and an inset smaller dial similarly divided into ten parts. Each of these dials has a single finger. Did Flamsteed then invent decimal time? The answer is that this is a clock designed to measure the angle of Earth's rotation relative to the distant "fixed" stars and it measures angles up to 360 degrees rather than the normal 24 hours of an ordinary clock.

Set in the face of the clock is a curved window, in which figures appear showing the number of tens of degrees through which the Earth has rotated since the angle was equivalent to time zero. Next, the outer dial indicates single degrees up to ten, with smaller sub-divisions each indicating ten minutes of arc. Then the smallest dial indicates very small angles up to ten minutes of arc for one complete revolution of the finger and has smaller sub-divisions, each representing ten seconds of arc. The clock would thus indicate the angle turned through by the Earth in degrees, minutes and tens of seconds of arc.

In the photograph. the sidereal clock indicates 30 degrees in the curved window, 1 degree 20 minutes on the peripheral dial and 30 seconds of arc on the smallest dial - a total angle of 31 degrees 20 minutes 30 seconds. This clock enabled Flamsteed to measure the east-west angle between two stars very accurately or to determine the angle of any star east or west of the Greenwich Meridian.

Figure 27.
Photograph of the face of Flamsteed's Sidereal or Angle Clock.

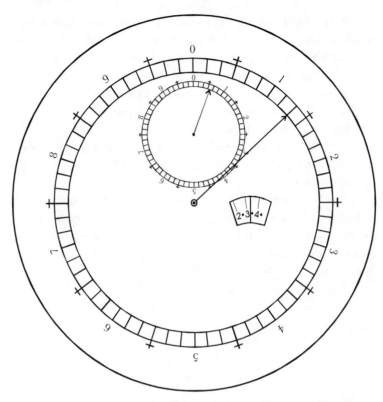

Figure 28.
Diagram of the face of Flamsteed's Sidereal or Angle Clock.

J. The Octagon Room at the Greenwich Observatory. (See figure 6, page 42)

This is the largest and most splendid room in the Royal Observatory at Greenwich and it is fortunate that an illustration of the room drawn by Francis Place, in about 1676, still exists to show something of how the room was laid out and used. In the etching the two Great Clocks are shown to the left of the entrance door and the other clock, perhaps constructed under Richard Towneley's direction, is to the right. The life-size full-length portraits of King Charles II and his brother, the Duke of York (afterwards King James II), are above the door.

On the right side of the etching an astronomer uses a long Keplerian telescope, which is supported on a "ladder" close to the window and on a trestle with a screw adjustment near the observer. The tall windows were designed to accommodate the long telescopes which were common in Flamsteed's day.

To the left, another astronomer uses a quadrant of about four feet radius to take the angle of an object in the sky. In the background, close to the clocks, a third man is seated at the table, noting down the time and observational details called out to him by the astronomers.

The Octagon Room, at the present day, has been fitted out in a similar way to that illustrated in Francis Place's etching and preserves the 17th Century appearance of this major room in the observatory.

Flamsteed's Assistants, Colleagues and Contemporaries

ARBUTHNOT, JOHN (1667-1735). A Scottish mathematician, physician and satirical writer, who moved to London soon after receiving his M.D. from St. Andrews University in 1696. He taught mathematics and was elected F.R.S. in 1704. In 1705, he happened to be present when Prince George suddenly became ill during a visit to Epsom and his medical attention to the Prince Consort on this occasion gained him Queen Anne's lasting gratitude and favour. He was physician to the Queen 1705 - 1714. In the early part of 1711, Dr. Arbuthnot was commanded by Queen Anne to oversee the final stages in the publication of the *Historia Coelestis* and he acted as intermediary between Flamsteed and Halley (who was directly involved in the publication as its principal editor), becoming embroiled in their disputes concerning the names of certain stars and into which constellation they properly belonged. These disagreements largely hinged upon niceties in the meaning of certain Greek or Latin words and phrases used by earlier astronomers and must have given Dr. Arbuthnot (who was basically a kind and helpful man) an almost impossible task.

BOSSLEY, WILLIAM. An apothecary who lived in Bakewell, Derbyshire, not far from Luke Leigh. He was an amateur astronomer and friend of John Flamsteed with a particular interest in the planets Jupiter, Saturn and Mars – corresponding with him in order to calculate the positions of these planets more accurately than could be found from the *Rudolphine Tables* or the *Caroline Tables*. He assisted Flamsteed as a calculator from 1696 but was not asked to do the same calculations as Luke Leigh since Flamsteed wanted to avoid any possibility of collusion between these near neighbours. Flamsteed preferred entirely independent calculations, one performed in Derbyshire and the other in London if possible, as a check on each other's results.

BURNET, GILBERT (1643-1715). Scottish theologian and historian who moved to London in 1674, publishing his *History of the Reformation* between 1679 and 1715. (It was probably a copy of this book which had belonged to John Flamsteed that Joseph Crosthwait gave to Abraham Sharp). Gilbert Burnet met William of Orange on the continent in 1684, encouraging William's seizure of the English throne in 1688, and was appointed Bishop of Salisbury by King William in 1689. He was a broad churchman, who attempted to unite Nonconformists with the Church of England.

CASSINI, GIOVANNI DOMENICO (1625-1712). Possibly the most famous astronomer of his time, Cassini, who was born in Italy, was invited to Paris by Louis XIV in 1669 to join the *Academie Royale des Sciences* and in 1670 was made the first Director of the new Paris Observatory. He discovered four of Saturn's satellites as well as the dark gap in Saturn's rings, known as the Cassini Division. He also measured the rotation rate of Jupiter and Mars and began work on measuring the arc of the meridian (the line of longitude) through Paris by accurate ground surveying. Flamsteed was invited by the Royal Society to become their correspondent with G-D Cassini, in an effort to demonstrate that British astronomers were of comparable ability to the French.

CASSINI, JACQUES (1677-1756). Son of G-D Cassini, following him as Director of the Paris Observatory in 1712. He travelled widely and when in England, met Newton, Halley and Flamsteed and was elected a member of the Royal Society. He disagreed with Newton over his Gravitational Theory and with Flamsteed over the measurement of stellar parallax. He completed the measurement of the arc of the meridian between Dunkirk and Perpignan begun by his father.

CASWELL, JOHN (1655-1712). A trusted correspondent of Flamsteed, who had graduated with an M.A. from Wadham

College, Oxford, in 1677. He became Vice-Principal of Hart Hall (one of Oxford's oldest colleges which later became Hertford College in 1740). Caswell was Savilian Professor of Astronomy 1709-1712, whilst Halley was Savilian Professor of Geometry.

CLOWES, SAMUEL. An indentured assistant at the Royal Observatory from 1691, whose origins were in Wirksworth, Derbyshire. He was involved in the calculation of the Moon's positions when these were requested by Newton in 1694 but possibly finding this work quite tedious and boring, he absconded from Flamsteed's service in February 1695. Later he became surveyor to the city of New York.

COLLINS, JOHN. Fellow of the Royal Society, with an interest in navigation and mathematics which he had originally learnt whilst serving with the Venetians during their war with the Turks. Although he was not a practising astronomer himself he was very impressed with the early work of John Flamsteed and was instrumental in introducing Flamsteed to Sir Jonas Moore. This meeting later lead on to Flamsteed's appointment as Astronomer Royal.

CROMPTON, JAMES. Fellow of Jesus College, Cambridge, to whom Flamsteed communicated his observations of the great comet of 1680-81 and which led to the arguments between Isaac Newton and Flamsteed concerning the paths taken by comets.

CROSTHWAIT, JOSEPH. A native of Cumberland who became Flamsteed's assistant probably in 1709 after Isaac Wolferman left. He was a capable mathematician who could calculate star positions accurately from the raw data and also calculated positions of the Moon as a check on Abraham Ryley's results. He continued at the observatory until the death of John Flamsteed in 1719, giving Margaret Flamsteed much-needed support at this difficult time, and then, out of respect for his former employer and with the help of Abraham Sharp, was instrumental in getting Flamsteed's results finished and seen through to the final publications of 1725 and 1729.

DENTON, CUTHBERT. Sent by Sir Jonas Moore to assist Flamsteed at Greenwich when the observatory was first opened, his job was to move equipment around and to assist with observations as directed.

GREGORY, DAVID (1661-1708). Was the nephew of James Gregory and followed him into the Professorship of Mathematics at St. Andrew's University. Later, he became Savilian Professor of Astronomy at Oxford. In 1702 Flamsteed wrote, "I believe you need not suspect his sincerity or abilities in anything of geometry, though his astronomy is poor. He is fitter for the other chair," (i.e. Geometry rather than Astronomy). Flamsteed disliked David Gregory, who was a good theoretician after the pattern of Newton rather than a practical astronomer. "He is a closet astronomer, never having thought of throwing away money on instruments." Flamsteed praised Gregory's book *De Horologia Oscillatorio* but attacked his *Elements of Astronomy*, commenting, "I do not believe many in the world will be the wiser for it." There was a clear rift between the practical astronomer and the theoretician Gregory but in matters such as that of the Earth's annual parallax Flamsteed was not always correct.

GREGORY, JAMES (1638-1675). Scottish mathematician and astronomer who became Professor of Mathematics at St. Andrew's University (1669-1674) and then at Edinburgh University (1674-1675). In 1663, he described the Gregorian pattern of reflecting telescope but never succeeded in making one. In July 1673, he asked Flamsteed for advice on what equipment to install at the new St. Andrew's observatory.

HODGSON, JAMES. A relative of Sir Christopher Wren, Hodgson was a capable mathematician who assisted Flamsteed after Abraham Sharp left the observatory. He was paid £6.16s.6d. for three months work, April-June 1698, or a rate of 26 guineas per annum. In 1702 he married Flamsteed's niece Anne and became a mathematics teacher in London. He was elected a Fellow of the Royal Society on the same day in 1703 on which Sir Isaac Newton became its President. He became the Mathematics Master at Christ's Hospital in 1708, (continuing in this post until his death in 1755), and performed calculations for Flamsteed that were a check on Luke Leigh. He seems to have been a quiet person who, whilst loyal to Flamsteed, was careful not to antagonise those of influence in the Royal Society.

LEIGH, LUKE. An impoverished relative of Edmond Halley, who lived in Derbyshire near William Bossley. He was a reliable mathematician and after tuition by Flamsteed did sterling work as a calculator of star positions.

MOORE, SIR JONAS (1617-1679). A north countryman, born at Whitelee in Pendle Forest, Lancashire. During the Civil War, he used the library of the antiquarian Christopher Towneley, where the papers of William Gascoigne, Jeremiah Horrocks and other northern astronomers were preserved. He taught mathematics in London and published the first edition of *Moore's Arithmetick* in 1650. He was employed as surveyor during the drainage of the East-Anglian fens from 1649 and went to Tangiers, in 1663, to survey for the planned fortifications of that city. In 1669 he was appointed Surveyor-General of Ordnance and given extensive accommodation in a house inside the grounds of the Tower of London. He was knighted in 1673 and became the patron of the young John Flamsteed. Also in 1673 Moore was responsible, with others, for establishing the 'Royal Mathematical School' within Christ's Hospital to teach navigation to young men intending to enter the King's service at sea.

NORTH, SIR FRANCIS (1637-1685). Had a distinguished career in politics, becoming Attorney-General 1673-1675, Lord Chief Justice 1675-1682, and Lord Chancellor 1682-1685. He was created Baron Guildford in 1683 and was instrumental in appointing John Flamsteed to the living of the Parish of Burstow in 1684.

OUGHTRED, WILLIAM (1575-1660). The son of a writing master at Eton College, who was taught by his father and won a scholarship to that college. He afterwards became a Fellow of

King's College, Cambridge and the author of the mathematical *Canon* which Flamsteed used during his early studies at home. Oughtred, as well as being the rector of a parish in Surrey, was a notable teacher of such men as Sir Christopher Wren, Sir Jonas Moore and Professor Seth Ward.

PLACE, FRANCIS (1647-1728). A country gentleman who lived much of his time in York, Francis Place had earlier studied Law in London and had there developed a love of the fine arts, becoming the pupil and friend of the accomplished etcher Wenceslaus Hollar (1607-1677). Hollar seems to have received Thacker's drawings of the Royal Observatory for etching but being generally overworked probably passed on this commission to his pupil Francis Place. It is therefore Francis Place's etchings, based on Thacker's drawings, which have preserved for us the appearance of the Observatory soon after its completion and some of Flamsteed's astronomical instruments.

POUND, JAMES (1669-1724). A medical graduate and keen amateur astronomer, who became a chaplain to the East India Company. He travelled widely in the Far East, visiting India, China and Cambodia. In 1700, Flamsteed sent him a quadrant which he had specially bought and calibrated, together with the positions of 62 stars visible in the southern sky which could be used as references in compiling a southern star catalogue. These items took three years to reach him. In 1705, Pound was attacked in a British settlement by local tribesmen, escaping clad only in his night-shirt and losing all his observations but eventually he reached Batavia (modern Djakarta in Indonesia) safely. He became Rector of Wanstead, Essex, a parish some six miles north of Greenwich, where he had a 123-foot telescope suspended from the maypole. Joseph Crosthwait examined this instrument but did not recommend its design. The Revd. Pound later succeeded Flamsteed as Rector of Burstow in 1720. He was asked to make a Latin translation of Flamsteed's preface to the *Historia Coelestis Britannica*, but was so slow at performing this task that it was taken out of his hands.

RYLEY, ABRAHAM. A pupil of Flamsteed and James Hodgson who lived at Greenwich and helped in the calculation of stars in certain constellations from 1705 to 1708. He died about six days before Flamsteed in 1719.

SHARP, ABRAHAM. Another north countryman, born at Little Horton near Bradford in Yorkshire in 1653. He assisted Flamsteed for six months during 1684 and was appointed to a more permanent post on the death of John Stafford. Flamsteed praised him as "an excellent geometrician and mathematician" and also as "a most expert and curious mechanic." He constructed the Mural Arc, which involved 14 months work and cost over £200, which was so successfully used from 1689. He left Greenwich to teach mathematics in London and then worked for the Ordnance Office in Portsmouth but he continued to keep in touch with Flamsteed and in 1702, offered to assist with the calculation of star positions from Flamsteed's raw data - a task which entailed about one hour's careful work for each observation. Sharp retired to his home in the isolated village of Little Horton, but continued to correspond with Flamsteed and carry out calculations for him. He published the mathematical text book *Geometry Improved,* in 1717. Sharp understood Flamsteed's methods better than any other person and it is very largely due to his support of Joseph Crosthwait in calculations, drawings and editorial work, that Flamsteed's catalogues and star charts were eventually published.

SHERBURNE, SIR EDWARD (1618-1702). Was Clerk of the Ordnance but in 1687 he was removed from this post due to his suspected Roman Catholic tendencies. He was a friend of the Lancashire Towneleys, who were also Roman Catholics.

SMITH, THOMAS. Flamsteed's first assistant at the Royal Observatory, moving in with Flamsteed, in 1676, to help with observational work as directed. He left, in 1684, to take a post with the Ordnance Office at the Tower of London and later became the storekeeper for the Office of Ordnance at Chatham.

Stafford, John. Flamsteed's assistant who died in May 1688, after working at the observatory for nearly four years.

Streete, Thomas (1621-1689). The author of *Astronomia Carolina* (1661), a notable text book used in Flamsteed's early days.

Thacker, Robert. An artist employed by King Charles II from 1673 at a salary of £60 per annum, "to draw drafts of the principal forts and other matters concerning fortifications," and therefore well known to Sir Jonas Moore (Surveyor-General of Ordnance). Thacker's drawings of the Royal Observatory, made soon after its completion, were probably passed on for etching to Wenceslaus Hollar (1607-1677) who was one of London's first and most accomplished etchers. These drawings give us an excellent record of the Observatory and some of Flamsteed's astronomical instruments.

Tompion, Thomas (1638-1713). The instrument maker and clock-maker for Sir Jonas Moore, who made the two Great Clocks for the Greenwich Observatory, in 1676, and the Sidereal Clock for John Flamsteed, in 1691.

Towneley, Richard. The nephew of Christopher Towneley, the Lancashire antiquarian who kept the scientific papers of William Gascoigne, Jeremiah Horrocks, etc. The Towneleys were Roman Catholics of the landed gentry, whose family seat was at Towneley Hall near Burnley and were able to employ a servant to help in their scientific work and astronomical observations. This servant showed John Flamsteed their equipment during his visit in 1670 and in 1672 Flamsteed joined Richard Towneley in observations of Mars.

Vansomer, Paul. An excellent, although elderly draughtsman who could produce accurate star charts, employed by Flamsteed to draw star maps during the years 1703 to 1704.

Wallis, John (1616-1703). Savilian Professor of Geometry at Oxford and author of many mathematical books. Of particular importance was *Opera Mathematica*, Volume III, of 1699 which contained Flamsteed's attempt at the measurement of stellar parallax.

WARD, SETH (1617-1689). Savilian Professor of Astronomy at Oxford, 1649 - 1661, afterwards becoming Bishop of Salisbury whilst retaining his interest in astronomy. He was one of the Commissioners who was involved in the foundation of the Greenwich Observatory and a courtier to whom Flamsteed looked for patronage after the death of Sir Jonas Moore.

WESTON, THOMAS. Came to Flamsteed as "an ingenious but sickly youth" who later showed his abilities as an accurate observer at the Royal Observatory who could also draw the constellations accurately and produce good star charts. He is probably the only one of Flamsteed's assistants whose picture has been preserved, since his portrait along with that of John Flamsteed appears on the south-east corner of the ceiling of the Painted Hall at the Royal Naval College in Greenwich.

WITTY, JOHN. Another of Flamsteed's students who became his assistant during the period around 1705-1706 when pressure to publish Flamsteed's results became intense. He was paid £5.7s.6d. for one quarter's work in 1705 but was dismissed, in May 1706, with exactly £5 for one quarter's work. Flamsteed compared Witty's results with those calculated by Abraham Sharp and recalculated them himself if the answers differed by more than 5 seconds of arc. Witty afterwards became chaplain to the Wallop family in Hurstbourne, Hampshire, who employed him "on better terms than I could afford him," said Flamsteed. It was in response to Flamsteed's written statement regarding sums paid to John Witty and Thomas Weston that Sir Isaac Newton and Dr. Arbuthnot granted Flamsteed £125 from the monies they received from Prince George for the costs of producing Flamsteed's catalogue.

WOLFERMAN, ISAAC. Another of Flamsteed's students who became an assistant at the Greenwich Observatory. He was referred to by Flamsteed as "my amanuensis" and "my domestic servant" but in reality he was one of the assistants who proved useful in calculations during the period 1705-1708. He left, in February 1709, for a military career.

WREN, SIR CHRISTOPHER (1632-1723). One of the brightest men of his day who excelled in many fields. He was greatly respected by Flamsteed who wrote, "He is a very sincere, honest man. I find him so, and perhaps the only honest person I have to deal with". Flamsteed was perhaps too bold in comparing his own work with that of Wren when in a letter to Sir Christopher he writes, "Some betray their ignorance by asking why I do not print [my data]. They may as well ask why St. Paul's is not finished!"

WROE, RICHARD (1641-1718). Originally from Prestwich, Lancashire, Wroe became a Fellow of Jesus College, Cambridge. He corresponded with Flamsteed between 1670 and 1674.

Concise Bibliography

1. *An Account of the Revd. John Flamsteed*, by Francis Baily. London, 1835. Reprinted by Dawson's of Pall Mall, London, 1966.

2. *The Correspondence of John Flamsteed, First Astronomer Royal*, edited by Eric G Forbes, Lesley Murdin and Frances Willmoth. Institute of Physics Publishing, Bristol and Philadelphia, 1995.

3. *Greenwich Time and the Discovery of the Longitude*, by Derek Howse. Oxford University Press, 1980.

4. *The Gresham Lectures of John Flamsteed*, edited by Eric G Forbes. Mansell, London, 1975.

5. *The Preface to John Flamsteed's Historia Coelestis Britannica or British Catalogue of the Heavens (1725)*, edited by Allan Chapman, translated by Alison D Johnson. London, 1982.

6. *Greenwich Observatory: 1675 - 1975, Vol. I. Origins and Early History*, by Eric G Forbes. Taylor and Francis, London, 1975.

7. *Greenwich Observatory; 1675 - 1975, Vol. III. The Buildings and Instruments*, by Derek Howse. Taylor and Francis, London, 1975.

8. *Dividing the Circle. The development of critical angular measurement in astronomy, 1500 - 1850*, by Allan Chapman. Horwood, New York and London, 1990.

9. *Geared to the Stars*, by Henry C King in collaboration with John R Millburn. University of Toronto Press, 1978.

10. *Francis Place and the Early History of the Greenwich Observatory*, by Derek Howse. New York, 1975.

11. *Sir Jonas Moore: Practical Mathematics and Restoration Science*, by Frances Willmoth. The Boydell Press, Woodbridge, 1993.

12. *Flamsteed's Stars*, edited by Frances Willmoth. The Boydell Press, Woodbridge, 1997.